# Freedom from Anxiety

An Revolutionary 10-Minute
Process Returning Clarity and
Ease to Your Life

By

## Dr. Johnny Kenley

# FREEDOM FROM ANXIETY

Copyright 2015 by **DR. JOHNNY KENLEY**

Printed in the United States of America.

First Printing: Summer 2015

# Dedication

This book is dedicated to all of my former patients for all that they have taught me. It is especially dedicated to the approximately 2,400 patients and clients over the last 4 years in Kenya, Tanzania, China, Russia, India, and the Philippines. I have had the honor to assist them with their emotional issues (anxiety, stress, and fear). Without them, the REIN process would have never evolved. It is also dedicated to my daughter Jessica and my beloved, Janice.

# Acknowledgments

I would like to extend sincere appreciation to the truck driver who ran me over many years ago in 2002. Had it not been for my devastating injuries, I would have remained on the same, somewhat self-centered path of accumulation, ego gratification, and looking outward for meaning. The ensuing 4 years of neurocognitive rehabilitation were like a reset—offering a rare opportunity for rebirth using heretofore acquired education, knowledge, and training, and blending that with the experience of tens of thousands of hours of precious doctor–patient interaction. For each and every one of my patients, clients, indigents, and jailed, I am humbly grateful to have known them. It is I that am better for that. Physicians, psychologists, therapists, colleagues, close friends, and even acquaintances were all incredibly supportive during that long, long rehabilitation. My best friend Dr. Ray Nietzold, while far away, was always a pillar of absolute loving support. My dear longtime close friend and colleague Dr. Alan Korbett, psychiatrist, was a rock in guidance, so incredibly knowledgeable and caring. I would like to express appreciation for my loving, wise mentor Dr. Barbara Stone.

I have come to realize that maybe there are no new ideas, but that ideas, certainly of noble intent, reside in a Universal Consciousness. To that end, over a few centuries, when these ideas came the conscious awareness of a few individuals, they had no choice but to take these ideas, precepts, concepts, and understandings now imbued in them and act. They acted by remolding, reshaping these ideas in accordance with what resonated with them; they turned the old ideas into fresh content with enhanced expression, vibrant concepts, and new methods. They put all this to pen for us. These authors' intentions were to awaken and abet humankind so I'd like to extend an equally abundant amount of gratitude to perhaps about 700+ authors of my library collection—4 years of reading, re-reading, reading aloud, and reading again created such an explosive synthesis, understanding, and especially awareness. It was not just understanding, but a shift from *belief to knowing*—from looking outward to looking inward.

These authors include Osho (Bhagwan Shree Rajneesh), Saint Thomas Aquinas, Gautama Buddha, Pantanjali, Helen Cohn Schucman and William Thetford, Anthony Robbins, Martin Luther King, Lao Tzu, Napoleon Hill, Deepak Chopra, Dr. Wayne Dyer, George Carlin, Thich Nhat Hanh, Eckart Tolle, Henry David Thoreau, Og Mandino, Ernest Holmes, Dale Carnegie, Voltaire, Milton Erickson, James Allen, Aristotle, George Santyana, Rev. Robert Schuller, Krishmamuriti, Dr. Jerry Jampolsky, and Fr. Anthony De Mello—a Jesuit priest and psychotherapist of Indian heritage who was so adept at blending East and West, at blending Buddha with Christ, with blending Bhagavad Gita, and with Christian scripture, extolling his readers to "wake up." I hope the reader would avail themselves of the opportunity for growth and awakening by reading any and all of these authors. They are authors but more so writing clarions to our awakening.

I wish to thank the people and organization of Bradley Communications (Steve Harrison, et al.) who were so instrumental in having avenues for getting authors to move their ideas and concepts forward. In this vein, I want to thank Ann McIndoo and company for having a process that rapidly gets a book from the person's mind to paper.

I have learned the books are *really* not written, but re-written and re-written and re-written; to that end, my gratitude to those assisting in the editing, namely Heidi Grauel and Deana Riddle for her interior design efforts. Additionally, Skye McKenzie's comments and advice was instrumental in getting the manuscript to print.

Lastly, I thank my beloved, Janice Arante, for her unwavering support.

# Contents

# Introduction

This book was written for people like you and me who deal with anxiety as a daily issue or problem that stops us from being fully engaged in life. Anxiety prevents us from daily enjoyment and the sweet juice of life that we all want. Anxiety keeps us contracted, tense, and in tension. Anxiety winds us tighter and tighter. In this un-resourceful state we are only capable of reacting—reflexively reacting in this anxiety state. If our emotional state of being is anxiety, we can only act as a reflex like when the doctor taps your knee—you just kick out, no alternative. We cannot come from a resourceful place—a place where we have a multitude of choices with which to face any situation that life presents—when we are living in anxiety.

Anxiety is such a common issue, and prevalent throughout all societies, therefore it seems reasonable for our purposes to call it a problem. To address a problem properly, it is important that we first define it clearly and concisely. What is anxiety? Is it different for different people? Is it a necessary evil? Isn't it a normal emotion? Are emotions themselves a necessary evil, especially those emotions we perceive as negative? Is anxiety part of a bigger problem? **Part One** of this book answers these questions and defines and shapes the emotional state of anxiety.

Once the problem is clearly defined, **Part Two** of this book explores how and where anxiety is structured. Where are the roots? Where are the branches? What are the conditions? To answer these questions, we look to these components: our body, our mind, and our body's energy systems.

Anxiety is not only not a new problem but it is also commonplace, so what then are the past and current approaches in dealing with this anxiety state of being? In **Part Three** of the book, we review several older and moderately older approaches as well as some cutting edge radical, newer approaches. They are only viewed as radical in the sense that they are not so readily accepted by the mental health establishment. The therapeutic approaches discussed are neither detailed nor exhaustive, but described to provide scope and perspective.

One perspective the astute reader might arrive at is being baffled. Given that in every society, in every country, in every age group, the state of being anxious is so commonplace—and growing almost exponentially in light of "established" available solutions—it makes one wonder why. In the final chapters of the book, a really outrageous approach to solving anxiety called REIN *(Resolving Emotional Issues Now)* is thoroughly described and outlined. The REIN process solution is clearly explained in a step-by-step process for the reader's immediate use: to immediately test, to immediately verify the effectiveness, and to immediately feel relief and amazement.

The book's three parts define the problem; clarify the problem's structure relative to our mind, our body, and our body's energy systems; and give background of past and current traditional solutions as well as the cutting edge approach of Energy Psychology. And, subsequently, we are led to the book's purpose: to present the reader with an understandable cogent solution, the step-by-step process of REIN, where people like you and me can resolve anxiety immediately, or at least lessen it so it is not affecting a deservedly joyful life. The REIN process is one that you can test, and you will know its effectiveness immediately along with the duration of that efficacy. REIN is a synthesis of Applied Kinesiology, clinical acupuncture, many different Energy Psychology methods, many cognitive processes, and neuro-linguistic programing (NLP) techniques. It has been designed, used, refined, and tested on more than 2,400 clients in 8 countries on 4 continents, and taught to hundreds of people with outstanding success and permanent results.

This book is not about theory—this is not an academic endeavor. This is about providing people like you and me with **an immediate but enduring approach for rapidly easing or even resolving our anxiety state of being.**

# PART ONE
# THE PROBLEM

Anxiety is everywhere. Anxiety is an emotion, and it is generally thought of as a negative emotion. Is the problem anxiety, the emotion of anxiety, or emotions themselves? I have not met anyone who wants more anxiety. No one seems to say, "Please, I want more anxiety." However, the perception is that it is natural and normal and something we need to live with. It seems natural to be anxious about meeting someone new, taking on new projects, dealing with new changes in your life, or dealing the unknown. It is believed to be something to be "lived with"—a necessary evil.

Anxiety as a diagnostic disorder is the most common mental illness in the United States, affecting 40 million people. Worldwide estimates of anxiety approach 40% of the population. When we look at our families, our friends, colleagues, or ourselves we might guess it affects even more people. And, given the degree of poverty, war, famine, and instability throughout the world, it might seem reasonable to put these estimates of anxiety near 100%. Anxiety affects us all and anxiety limits our ability to act effectively or perhaps even responsibly in most situations.

There is a fundamental difference in having anxiety, having situational anxiety, and having anxiety as your normal state—that is, anxiety as your normal emotional state of being. Anxiety by itself is not the problem, but rather a normal emotion.

**The problem is: having anxiety as your natural state of being.**

1

If our emotional being—our perpetual daily emotional state—is one that is stuck in anxiety, then this is an obstacle to everything we want and a killer of all our potential joy.

Since anxiety is an emotion, is it reasonable to *leap* to the assumption that emotions themselves could be the issue? The answer is unequivocally no and, much to the contrary, emotions are the driving forces behind all that we do every minute of every day. Emotions need exploration and a spot light shinned upon them, given the conflicting messages and conditioning we receive from infancy foreword. Part One closely examines anxiety and emotions in general to help clarify and concentrate on defining the exact problem.

# Chapter 1
# Anxiety

## What Is Anxiety?

Anxiety disorders are the most commonly diagnosed psychological disorders in the United States, affecting 40 to 50 million people and hundreds of millions worldwide. In the United States, each year 8 million people are diagnosed with general anxiety disorder, 15 million with social anxiety, 19 million with phobias, and 7 million with panic disorder. In 2013, anxiety medications tallied 255,100,000 prescriptions, totaling tens of billions of dollars in sales. But, after the diagnoses and prescriptions, do we see any lessening of anxiety? It is not a question of whether you and I experience anxiety, we do. And, if you are reading this book, you recognize it's an issue that you'd like to address. It is then important to get at the heart of what it means to have anxiety, to live with it daily, and its detrimental effects, but most importantly the difference between anxiety and existing in a state of anxiety being.

It is necessary to have a common, agreed definition of what anxiety actually is. There is no lack of ways to define anxiety depending on which professional you ask, or the field of that professional. Anxiety is sometimes defined as a feeling of fear and of worry, of tension, or apprehension. Others depict it as a distress or uneasiness of the mind caused by fear. Another definition presents it as an unpleasant feeling of inner turmoil. It is also defined to be an unpleasant feeling or dread over anticipated events. As stated before, anxiety is often described as a feeling of worry and fear. But, what is fear? How is fear defined? One definition is that it is an anxious feeling caused by our anticipation of some event, either real or imagined—but this defines anxiety in terms of fear, and fear in terms of anxiety. Other definitions of both anxiety and fear relate to something distressing (by an impending real or imagined danger-pain) and further accompanied by a sensation of agitation and dread caused by some imminent danger.

Besides distressing, additionally when we experience anxiety, we also use the word *stress*. So, how is stress defined? Some authorities define stress as a reaction to anything that disturbs our normal equilibrium. Also, it has been characterized in terms of a response to something very specific that is creating anxiety and fear.

Now you may wonder, *Am I fearful? Am I stressed?* or *Am I anxious?* Are they all interrelated? Are they interchangeable? The answer is yes and no. All three of these are simply **words** that we have assigned to particular feelings in response to situations that happen to us. Even though one person can say, "I have lots of *anxiety* about a certain situation," another person may describe their feeling, in that same situation, as *stressed* or even that they were feeling *fear*—similarly with stress or with being fearful or afraid—these fluid, interconnected definitions make them inter-relatable.

If you are anxious, you are fearful of something happening, and if you are fearful, then you have anxiety, and if you are stressed, then there is a change in your equilibrium—something has happened out of the ordinary for you—and you have anxiety about it, and may well feel fearful. Thus, we have anxiety, stress, and fear as typical expressions for our "sensed" emotion, or aspects of some of the wealth of emotions that we experience every hour of the day, sometimes even every minute of the day.

This book could have been entitled *Freedom from Fear* or *Freedom from Stress*—however, we use *anxiety* since this is a term that is in line with our own self-talk and it seems safe for us to discuss with others. In reality . . . **Anxiety is essentially a shade of fear, a degree of fear**. And it is a natural valuable emotion that we sense continually throughout our day. However, having anxiety as your natural state of being is not only unhealthy, but keeps us immobile or, conversely, just a hyperactive reflex to life.

## The Emotional Rainbow

Once we've labeled something as a problem, how does this problem show up in our life? How exactly do we find ourselves in this state of anxiety? When we think about anxiety, it is not about simply experiencing anxiety but rather how an anxiety state of being becomes the place on our emotional spectrum where we get stuck— that is, the emotional state of being where we spend most of our time. The terms rainbow, spectrum, continuum , and range relating emotions are interchangeable.

Let's look at the range of all our emotions—all those positive emotions and all those negative emotions that are part and parcel of our entire being. Think of this range as a continuous line and, at one end, we will put "fear." At the other end of the spectrum, for simplicity, we may want to put happy or, better yet, loving bliss. Illustration 1 is simply a line that is a representation of this emotional spectrum or continuum. We can think of this line as the continuum of emotions, because there are almost unlimited points along this line where we could use and place a word that describes some emotion between fear and loving bliss.

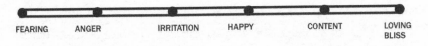

| FEARING | ANGER | | IRRITATION | HAPPY | | CONTENT | | LOVING BLISS |

Illustration 1: Emotional continuum.

Looking at this continuum of emotions, anxiety could be placed somewhere along this line, away from fear (but, know, it is a degree of fear). If you are anxious, you are fearful of something. Similarly, stress could be placed along this line, because if you are stressed you are anxious, and if you are anxious you are fearful.

So, these two emotions—anxiety and stress—are degrees, or shades of fear as we move along the line—and this line is an emotional continuum. Incidentally, in our daily life, we are either moving toward fear (or stuck in fear) or moving toward contentment and loving bliss. In other words, you are either loving or fearing. Anxiety is a point on that line representing a shade or degree of fear. We are continually moving on that line minute by minute throughout our day. Every single day in real time, we experience wide ranges of emotions perceived as good to neutral to bad. These emotions are part of our daily lives. All these emotions are healthy and natural.

## Anxiety Conditioning

It may seem inconceivable but there are those who actually think or even tell us that having anxiety (or having stress or being a little fearful) is a good thing. It is said to be motivating factor. It can move us off our duffs. I don't subscribe to this. I do think that a resourceful person can take any particular situation where they may feel anxiety (or stress or fear) and take that lemon and make lemonade. There is no question about that; however, most of us are trying to reduce our fear, anxiety, and stress.

Who is it who determines the value of anxiety or stress as degrees or shades of fear? We are conditioned by our MFTP—mother, father, teacher, preacher—and we are conditioned by our culture. These programmed forces often say the emotions of anxiety, stress, and fear are beneficial. They suggest this essentially because it propagates the status quo. Our conditioning therefore is centered around anxiety and fear.

Even with our programmed guise of anxiety being potentially beneficial, we do attempt to reduce our anxiety, and sadly do so by use of a variety of products and methods in order to cope—whether it be food (sugar and fats), drugs (legal or illegal), alcohol, or obsessive activities or compulsions. Although, inherently, our emotional state of being is not anxiety, our conditioning has altered virtually everyone so much so that a contented or happy person is viewed as not grasping the *realities* of life. Anxiety is a natural emotion, but existing in an emotional state of anxiety is not natural, although prevalent.

Let's return to our simplified graphical representation (this single line) of our emotional continuum. We can tilt this line a little bit so that we have a slope shown in Illustration 2.

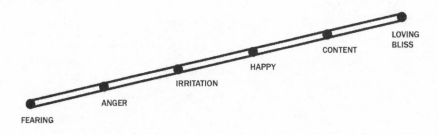

Illustration 2: Sloped emotional continuum.

This tilting represents the beginning of our conditioning. On one end we still have fear but now sloping upward at the other end of the line remains loving bliss. If it remained level, moving in either direction would be equally easy. But if tilted up to the right, we can see it is harder to go up toward being happy—it is much easier to slide down with almost no effort. We are either moving in the direction of fearing down to the left, or we are moving upward in the direction of loving up to the right. We move along this line all day, perhaps thousands of times a day. Since our initial conditioning favors one direction—fearing—we tilt the line.

## A Dwelling Place

In Illustration 3, we see hypothetically what our emotional line is at birth and then at different times as we proceed through life with our conditioning, experiences, traumas, and growth. Loving bliss remains at the right end of spectrum. In the illustration, (a) represents the continuum at birth. In (b) we see that it is more challenging to move toward happiness or loving bliss and easier to drift downward toward fear. This is a function of the beginning of our conditioning and experiences. In (c) we see a gap has occurred, because of a single event or even multiple traumas. Here you can see that some additional energetic momentum is required to even get to that upper line. In (d) and (e) more continuing life traumas and reinforced conditioning are shown creating larger gaps and changes in the slope. This prohibits movement toward bliss, and conversely shows how easy it is to keep falling into fear. Certainly, the slopes of those lines are different, and for each person the slopes are different. The slopes of the line may be a function of that individual's genetics, of that person's life story, and of their particular conditioning that has happened to them. The gap relates to a trauma or repetition of similar traumas. All this also may be a function of the epigenetics—ongoing things that have occurred in their lives over months or years. No two people have the same slope(s).

PART ONE **THE PROBLEM**

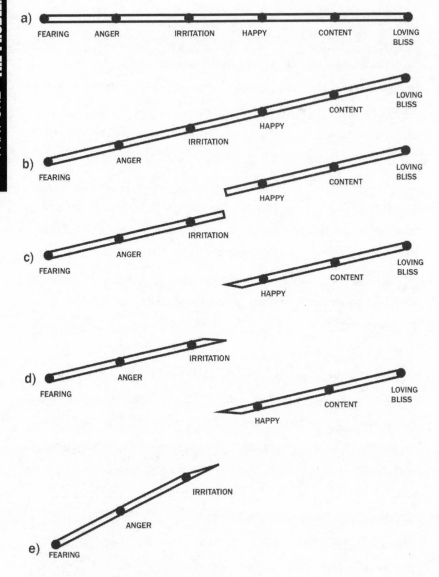

Illustration 3: Emotional continuum(s) across time.

In Illustration 4, we can further modify the line, putting little wells along each of these lines to show the different emotions demonstrating increasing chance of getting stuck in any particular "well." We are going to put just a few of these in, rather than all of the hundreds or thousands of emotions that we experience.

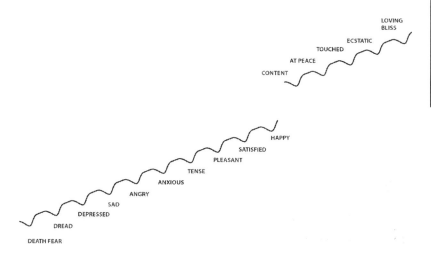

Illustration 4: Emotional continuum expanded.

This provides us with an improved representation from that shown in Illustration 1. It continues to demonstrate that with this upward slope, it is easier to slide down to the left toward fearing than it is to fight upward to the right, happy or loving or blissful. And, it shows the gap between one line and the other line. As stated before, this usually represents a significant event or trauma that has happened in our lives—some radical change that caused a break in our emotional continuum that now keeps us from readily moving up to the second line. We can be and are at any place along the bottom line and make a change up to the top line, and vice versa. We can be on that top line and something can happen and bring us down to the other—and all this literally happens in seconds or minutes as our day goes on. This is our daily emotional continuum.

Now importantly, Illustration 4 demonstrates that we can stay in one particular emotional state of being, the little wells, as our resting place. As previously stated, we can and certainly do move up or down the continuum, but we generally return to our normal emotional state of being—this little well. Again, we are defining this well as the emotional state that we predominantly stay in, not merely having that emotion. Our resting state might be a contented state; it might be an irritated state; it may be an angry state; it may be a satisfied state. This is then our normal emotional state—not that we do not have other emotions by the minute, or hourly, each day, but that is the place we end up residing.

In the Western society in which we live, and even in the Eastern societies, it is more common for people to exist in emotional states down the slope to the left, that is toward fearing—people's emotional states are more fearing than anything else. Perhaps it is only a state of being perplexed or confused; maybe it is in a state of being stressed. Maybe it is being in the emotional state of being anxious all the time. But, most of us do not live in the natural emotional states of the upper right slope—a sad indictment indeed.

## Conclusion

Most living organisms, including human beings, do have an instinct for survival, and this instinct means that we want to move toward the positive and away from the negative; for us, we want to be moving up the slope to the right rather than down the slope to the left. The preference is innate within us all, given the person is mentally healthy—we act to sustain the fight for survival. We can see visually and graphically that residing in an anxious state of being means living in fear, and there is effort required in order to move us in the opposite direction, toward being happy, or trying to overcome that gap moving toward being loving and finding bliss.

It is possible for us to find a different emotional state of being without the use of drugs and without the use of another person and without it taking months or years. Our natural state is not an anxious state. Our natural state is not a state of fear. Our natural being is a state of loving.

**Key Points to Remember:**

- Having emotions is normal.

- All emotions are healthy.

- Fear is a natural and normal emotion.

- Anxiety or being situationally anxious is normal.

- Anxiety is a shade or degree of fear.

- Living in an anxious emotional state of being is neither normal nor healthy.

# Chapter 2
# Emotions: Love Them or Leave Them

Anxiety, while natural, is not a healthy emotional state in which to reside. Any stuck emotional states of being, like anxiety, come from our conditioning—both familial and cultural, and/or from trauma. Does anxiety even exist within our bodies? And how does anxiety affect our body? Since emotions are the driving force for all that we do, it is crucial to understand how and where we come to experience our emotions—our individual emotional expression—and, perhaps, even more importantly, our awareness of our own emotional state of being.

## Emotions in the Body

While certainly emotions are simply feelings, there are many different ways of viewing emotions, and there are many different psychological, philosophical, and commonly accepted definitions. Each definition corresponds to the intended purpose specific to someone or to the psychiatrist's, psychologist's, or philosopher's model. At first glimpse one might think emotions are of or in the mind, but this is completely untrue. Regardless of what emotion, it is within our body that emotions are experienced—it is a biological or physiological expression. Emotions represent an agitation—a physiological and biological reaction within our bodies. (Physiological is regarding the workings of the body.) Where in the body? Everywhere, everywhere, everywhere. This means every single of our 100 trillion cells. It means within our physical brain and its inherent control systems (neuromuscular, neuroendocrine, neuroimmune), our skin, our glands, our organs, intestines, bones, muscles, connective tissue, fluids, immune system, and sensory organs of touch, smell, hearing, sight, taste. Emotions have their ultimate destination in our body— the absolute entirety of our body.

Perhaps this distinction has not been obvious to us, nor even something we gave even a passing thought. However, emotions dwell in our bodies.

A feeling is something felt. When you feel a particular emotion, either a negative or a positive emotion, it affects the entire body. For example, if you were sensing the emotion of comfort, you would have a response within every one of your cells. The response is manifested in the neurology of your brain and in the hormones of your brain—all of them—and in all of your musculature. This is instantaneous, literally within a few thousandths of a second. There would be relaxation. There would be body fluid changes. The immune system would change. All of your senses would change along with the working of your heart, lungs, liver, pancreas, and kidneys. The gut would change. Everything changes, and then this is a "set pattern" revealed by your body; it is a physiological reaction to the emotion of comfort. Comfort is not only felt by you, but it is sensed or seen by everyone—consciously or unconsciously.

If the emotion is anxiety instead of comfort, you wind up with another residual pattern displayed by and within your entire physical body, within the physical brain, within the neuroendocrine system, within the immune system. The muscles would contract differently—a whole different pattern would be represented and seen. *Everything* would change. And this too, is felt by you to the degree of your self-awareness, and it is sensed or seen by everyone consciously or unconsciously.

## All Emotions

So, then, besides anxiety, what other emotions do we experience? Are they limited or unlimited? In ancient traditional Chinese medicine or their philosophical literature, there are six emotions, namely:

- Anger
- Fear
- Fright
- Grief
- Joy
- Worry

16

Later, Aristotle spoke to 14:

- Anger
- Mildness
- Love
- Enmity
- Fear
- Confidence
- Shame
- Shamelessness
- Benevolence
- Pity
- Indignation
- Envy
- Stimulation
- Contempt

Simultaneously, Hinduism has nine emotions, or Rasas:

- Erotic love
- Compassion
- Wonderment
- Peace
- Laughter
- Heroism

- Fear

- Disgust

- Anger

In the Middle Ages, Saint Thomas Aquinas, an eminent Catholic theologian, described nine emotions in four pairs of opposite polarity with the exception being anger, which was left unpaired. He described emotions in terms of being reactions to fundamental types of motion; motion then of course related to our body and parts therein.

Breaking things down to their basics (an analysis, in fact), we can relate the primary emotions to the primary colors, and further still, the whole range of emotions would be similar to the whole spectrum of colors—many thousands of different colors and hues, similarly many thousands of emotions. This is probably true and the number of emotions is perhaps only limited by our language and vocabulary. For each of us, there are many different perceived positive emotions from A to Z, including things like abundant or accepted, accomplished, appreciative, authentic, cooperative, believing, focused, helpful, purposeful, needs, noble, relaxed, serene, strong, successful, thankful, trusting, wealthy, worthy, zany. Similarly, we sense or feel many perceived negative emotions: alone, aloof, anguished, blaming, clumsy, conflicted, defensive, difficult, discouraged, doubtful, drained, empty, fearful, fragmented, guilty, impatient, insecure, jealous, lousy, nervous, moody, suffering, withdrawn, worry, wronged—

so very many. Again, these are all our English words for them, in our language, and I am sure that in each language more flavors emerge, or perhaps even less.

**We naturally regard our hundreds of emotions as either positive or negative, regardless of what the eventual outcome might be.** A "perceived positive" feeling, like feeling cared for, is a positive emotion, but it might create laziness, and then laziness might be perceived as negative, or this may be exactly what you need at a particular time and it ends in a positive result. Likewise, our "perceived negative" emotional states can be great motivators and instigators to move us in a positive direction. Being frustrated might cause us to seek solutions, take action, and feel fulfilled. Being obsessed, which is perceived to be negative, can lead us to success by virtue of constant action. If we are feeling incompetent, which is negative, this can also cause us to move toward action to improve our incompetency, to become better educated, more accomplished, which, of course, then leads to positive results.

We all know intuitively what a particular emotion means to us. We feel it. We sense it. Emotions are with us all the time. Emotions are the driving forces behind all that we do. I repeat this as it may not be readily apparent to us.

## EMOTIONS ARE THE DRIVING
## FORCES BEHIND ALL WE DO.

Emotions are the power that moves us to where we want to go or away from what we want to avoid. They are pushing us away from or pulling us toward something. They are generally moving us away from something negative and toward something positive—toward a perceived good for us.

## Living With Our Emotions

We cannot live without emotions. There is no choice. This is something that has not been taught to you. Emotion, in the simplest term as stated before, implies a feeling (a physiological reaction) and that is totally unique to each individual, regardless of what the emotion is. When we sense or feel an emotion like "worried," each of us has a physiological reaction that is different from another person's and certainly different from culture to culture. The displayed "worried" pattern within a body is unique to each person, although there may be some over-all similarities. Being "worried" implies a degree of fear, which is evidenced by contraction rather than relaxation.

Emotions are not of the mind, by the mind, or for the mind. Emotions are in the body—they reside in the body. When we have a held thought, there is a corresponding physiological response in our body; a *pattern* is displayed by the entirety of our body. The body's exhibited response *pattern* is called an emotion. Emotions are what compel us to action daily in everything that we do.

Every day, we feel hundreds of emotions, so what then is our emotional being, our emotional state of being? The emotional state of being (emotional state is used interchangeably) is that place or "well" where you might find yourself "stuck"—usually, on that bottom slope on the left (see Illustrations 2 to 4). Specifically, where you are stuck on that line, on that continuum of emotions, this is where you dwell most of the time, and this is your emotional state. You certainly can and do experience different emotions and move up or down along the continuum. But, this is different from your resting emotional state. Our residual emotional state is definitely different for each of us, but most of us dwell at some "well" on that continuum. However, it does not mean that our emotional state of being cannot change. It certainly can, and we are going to demonstrate how to do this later in this book, in Chapter 9. To be repetitious, because repetition is the mother of success, all emotions are perfect exactly as they are: *they are the driving forces of everything that we do.*

If your emotional state of being is residing someplace on that bottom slope heading toward fear, you may find yourself in the state of constant anxiety, constant worry, and feeling constantly nervous, constantly scared, constantly angry (and anger is just fear being expressed outward), or constantly sad (which is fear being expressed inward). Whenever we find ourselves, stuck in an emotional state down on that left-hand slope, it would seem both reasonable and beneficial for us to move upward toward the right, toward more happiness—not only move in that direction but maybe find ourselves someplace where our emotional being can be most of the time. However, that is a choice that a person can decide for themselves—that is, to stay where they are or move upward. Given there is some self-awareness, it would seem reasonable that most people would want to move their emotional state from being "stuck" along that continuum to the right, away from fear and toward loving bliss.

## Emotional Awareness

Unless we are really actually in a heightened or charged emotional state, it may be difficult to self-asses our basic resting emotional state—introspection is required. We could, in quiet sincerity, contemplate and fill in the statement, "I always seem to be _____," or you could, if really courageous, ask someone else to fill in the statement about yourself: "You always seem to be _____." This might reveal a stuck area of which you were not aware.

As an example, let us take the emotion of irritation. You may have awareness that "I always seem to be irritated." There is nothing wrong with being irritated. It is a natural response to something that might occur daily in your life, like annoying drivers you encounter on your commute to work. All of us may be irritated 50 times a day, but if that turns out to be the place that we exist in most of the time, then this becomes our emotional state of being. And, remember that irritation is a mild form of anger and anger, again, is fear that is expressed outward. So, we are really feeling fear, and not consciously acknowledging that as fear, thus we express it ourselves outwardly as anger (or, in our situation, a mild shade of fear called irritation).

When we find ourselves in this position, it becomes a "stuck negative emotional issue" for us, and our lingering resting point . . . our emotional state. It is a stuck emotional state because you are attached to it by a thick rubber band. You go all over experiencing all the other emotions, but you are always snapped back there, to an emotional state of being irritated. Again, having the emotion of irritation is natural. However, if our emotional being is irritation, then we are stuck being irritated all the time—not a resourceful state. As an emotion, irritation has a specific *pattern* on and within our body. This emotion of irritation is a physiological response, and every single part of our body responds—our neurology, our neuro-musculature, our immune systems, our hearts, our lungs, all our organs, our skin, and our senses. The body's total demonstrated response is a *pattern* for this irritation. You may or may not consciously sense this in you, but it is profoundly there. Others certainly sense it, see it—either consciously or unconsciously given their degree of awareness.

As mentioned previously, we are conditioned by MFTP and society. And, we receive positive reinforcement for one thing, and/or negative reinforcement for another; and, in growing up, "no" is the word we have heard more than anything else.

## Reinforcing Emotions

What emotions are bolstered or emphasized? Which emotions are suppressed, down played, or even squashed? This varies so immensely from family to family, culture to culture, one cannot generalize except that when we naturally express emotion, is it reinforced positively or is it reinforced negatively. While not speaking for everyone, perhaps we can look back and see what things we were told by our caretakers:

- Boys do not cry.
- Do not get angry.
- Don't be so emotional
- Don't be shy; speak up.
- Do not talk back.
- Girls do not yell.
- Do not act up in here.
- You should be seen, not heard.
- You should not be afraid.
- You should be ashamed.
- Do not look at me like that.
- Do not act like a baby.

There are so many more. I am sure that every person reading this could add to that list and make it three pages long. In general, we are also told, and it is reinforced, that

**We should control our emotions, or
that we should not be so emotional.**

Our society finds and reinforces this to women: do not be so emotional, do not wear your emotions on your sleeve, you are too emotional. In contrast, reinforcement for males in this society is to withhold emotion, control them very much: do not be expressive, keep a tight upper lip, do not let anyone know what you are feeling. You and I were not conditioned to the value of emotions, the awareness of them, nor the natural expression of them (obviously appropriately). We were not conditioned to simply and beautifully observe them.

## Conclusion

Remember that every emotion is a physiological response of the entirety of our body to a held thought. Whether or not it is readily expressed and openly expressed, that displayed response pattern is still within our body, our whole body. That young teenager who has fear—even when it has been reinforced not to show fear—still has a response pattern in their body. In actuality, by not fully expressing an emotion appropriately, it increases the intensity of that emotion within the body, more often than not to the detriment of the body.

The following key points need to understood and taken to heart:

- Emotions and your emotional state of being are not the same.

- Emotions have their final dwelling in your body. They reside there.

- We have hundreds, even thousands of emotions every day.

- All emotions are fine exactly as they are.

- There is no need to limit your emotions; you can express them appropriately.

- Emotions are the driving forces of your life.

- Your emotional state of being is where you emotionally reside primarily.

- In life, either you are moving toward loving or you are moving toward fearing.

- A "stuck" negative emotional state keeps you un-resourceful.

# PART TWO
# THE PROBLEM'S STRUCTURE

The problem we are addressing is anxiety—or, more correctly, the problem of our being in a state of anxiety and residing in anxiety most of the time. If we don't want anxiety as our constant companion, we have to look at how anxiety plays out in our **minds** and in our **bodies**. We can talk and write about anxiety and these are functions of our mind. But, then how much role does the mind play with anxiety? Also, because emotions reside in the body, can't we just directly look to our body to remedy the situation? Is anxiety generated by our mind-- thereby making the body a co-conspirator? Additionally, it would seem valuable to examine how our bodies' **energy systems** are possibly mixed in with the structure of the problem of anxiety.

There are three separate parts (mind, body, and the body's energy systems, and their interrelationship) to examine as we begin to look the problem of anxiety. First, we acknowledge and explore the **mind**; second, our incredible **bodies**; and, third, our unique **energy systems** of our bodies—the Aura, the Chakras, and traditional Chinese Meridians. By looking at these three parts, we can see how anxiety is structured—and ultimately how to possibly integrate these three parts in finding a real solution for dissolving our anxiety.

# Chapter 3
# The Mind

This first chapter of Part Two introduces the mind's role in how we experience, filter, and ultimately react to situational anxiety. We have a conscious mind and an unconscious mind and this chapter explores how these two parts unite, generating our reactions or programmed, patterned responses—responses that more than likely have been established over time and that must be brought to our awareness (if not overridden) if we are to dissolve our anxiety.

## The Value of Your Mind

There is no doubt that in both Eastern and Western societies the mind is greatly appreciated, but even more than appreciated, it is valued beyond any aspect of our being. We are enamored with the mind, the brain, with "thinking," with great memories, and with the relationship between the mind and brain. We seem to almost worship the mind. Not surprisingly, in the United States alone, there are hundreds of universities and institutes with tens of thousands of neuroscientists explaining, studying, dissecting, and analyzing the brain–mind.

In support of the mind, and creating improved minds, nations are committed to their educational systems, the purpose of which is obviously to maintain their society as it is, to then keep it safe, and to keep it growing (primarily economically). To that end, educational systems are set up and directed solely at our minds. We are "educated" as people and students, to amass as much information as possible—the more, the better—and the prized one is that person that attains the most important. We think a person with vast amounts of stored information as *intelligent* and one with little as *stupid*. We want children's minds stuffed with facts, from algebra to zoology, and from mundane to inane. The more they can store and recall quickly at will, the greater the child is appreciated.

The acute and intensive focus is on storage of information and retrieval of information. It is also about the idea of thinking or reasoning, which *supposedly* assesses that information for value or conclusions—conclusions that reach decisions, hopefully for the better. The more highly educated you are, the more valued you are in society. The more intelligence, even if intelligence is poorly defined, the better. The higher your IQ, the more homage is paid to you.

People value your mind; they value your thinking process and they value the data that you can withdraw from your long-term memory (and the more and greater detailed, the better) as well as the speed in using perhaps an expanded short-term memory. People value your mind and language, your ability to speak, to use sentences, to express thoughts, and then write coherently as well to further express yourself. The mind is deemed crucial in any society that wants to exist with stability (as a minimum) or, preferably, to achieve greater development.

## Of Two Minds

*The Conscious Mind*

Let's talk about the mind in a slightly different way, not focusing just on intelligence and facts and the recall of facts. We are going to divide it into the conscious mind and the subconscious mind. We can, alternatively, use terms like our *unconscious*, or even *the not-conscious* mind. The subconscious mind sometimes includes this concept of an unconscious mind, so all three terms (subconscious, unconscious, and not-conscious mind) may be used here interchangeably. There are many, many models about this, but for our purpose, let's keep it simple: we will just say conscious and subconscious mind.

It is said that our conscious mind utilizes but 20% of our brain's capacity. Capacity here is related to the quantity of stored information and meaningful and logical use of that information—that is thinking. The conscious mind also acknowledges awareness, both of ourselves and the surrounding environment—it has to do with intention and it has to do with receiving and interpreting all of our five senses, integrating these senses with our minds, and making *sense* of them so to speak. The conscious mind deals with the use of our short-term memory and with our ability to store and retrieve information in the long term. So, the conscious mind deals with what is termed executive function, which is what we can call thinking and all the descriptions of what that encompasses. It has to do with putting *stuff* together.

Many theorists have speculated that the mind may be

within our brain; however, this remains to be proven and unlikely to ever be so. If we look at the brain itself, it is a seven- or eight-pound fragile mass with 100 billion cells called neurons. It is fragile in that it cannot be deprived of oxygen for very long or it dies quickly. Given there is but a modicum of understanding of a simple worm's brain of just 300 neurons, there seems little chance of understanding our 100 billion neuron brain, nor the integration of our many *subsidiary brains* that consists of many ganglia (groups of thousands of neurons) throughout our body. It makes greater sense that the mind is within the entire body, our whole physical being.

The brain uses about 20% of the energy of our body's expenditures. In doing so, the brain creates a vast amount of electrical fields, which are readily seen on a medical machine called electroencephalogram. This brain recording device is attached to electrodes on our head and it shows the electrical activity and brain waves. This can be printed out on paper. The brain cells' network can be thought of as electrical circuits, but, incredibly, thinking and processing do not actually physically alter these circuits themselves. The same is true for the electrical mechanisms in storing short- and long-term memories. This is amazing for it has been shown to be neither an analog nor digital electronic process. It has its own—yet to be discovered—mechanisms.

Within this conscious mind comes the concept of intelligence. As stated before, we tend to think of intelligence as having a vast long-term memory, but it is more than that. Intelligence in the simplest terms can be thought of as our ability to reason—that is, our ability to think clearly and coherently, our ability to create and understand events occurring in real time as well as abstract concepts, to create short-term memory, and additionally having a long-term memory storage and retrieval capacity. Thinking, while a complicated organizing process, could be defined simply and operationally as merely a process of asking questions, comparative questions, thereby evaluating by contrasting to some standard. **Thinking can be viewed as the internal questioning, upon questioning, upon questioning.**

## The Subconscious Mind

What about the other part of our mind? The unconscious mind? What does our unconscious mind do? Our unconscious mind is really, really incredible. The most important parts of our existence—our ability to stay alive, to just function, to be—are placed in the hands not of the conscious mind, not of our thinking, not of our intellect, but within the realm of a part of the unconscious mind. Our intellect does not control our breathing, our heart rate, our rate of digestion, our absorption of nutrients, our disposal of waste, our immune system, nor anything that is critical to our survival.

None of the executive functions of the conscious mind have any control over the involuntary act of breathing, heart rate, etc. We breathe under control of our unconscious mind. Our heart rates, and how strongly our hearts beat, are controlled by the unconscious mind. We do not drive along the road and all of a sudden realize that our hearts have not pumped in the last 60 seconds and decide we are going to pump it, or make an analysis of whether we should pump blood or not. No, it is the unconscious mind that controls this.

The unconscious mind controls our digestive system, it controls the intake of our food, it controls how we want to eat, when we want to eat, what we like to eat, how that food is processed, how that food is digested, how it is secreted via our kidneys and colon. It controls our immune system. It controls our reproductive system. The unconscious mind controls the resting tone of the entirety of our musculature—all of the important systems of our bodies. It controls all of those things that keep us alive and keep us going forward. It is not the conscious mind or the intellect that does this. How ludicrous it would be to have the conscious mind controlling all of these functions—all of them simultaneously, millisecond by millisecond.

Sometimes, when the conscious mind decides to take control or to try to do something that alters the ability of our body, overriding the unconscious mind, problems usually ensue. It is not for the better. When the conscious mind decides to intake a pint of alcohol, take a drug because it doesn't like how the immune system is working, eat beyond what is needed, or hold one's breath—thereby speeding up or slowing down our systems synthetically— problems arise rapidly with a detrimental effect on the body.

Yes, the conscious mind can often attempt to exhibit control over the unconscious mind; but, the results usually are negative and devastating. If continuous control by the conscious mind is applied, usually death is the final result.

There is another critically important and massive role of the unconscious mind. Using computer analogies, the unconscious mind perhaps can be viewed as a hard drive, with enormous memory capacity while simultaneously internally running an entire set of independent programs. These programs are embedded in this hard drive. These programs are essentially representative of our conditioning that has occurred throughout our entire lives—the majority of the "programs" created before we even reach ten years of age.

It is important to understand that the unconscious mind has these fixed internal programs running continuously, and automatically. Even more importantly, it works without the awareness of the conscious mind or under the control of the conscious mind. Instead, they are continuously "controlling" our background.

## Programming, Reactions, and Control

These automatic programs of the subconscious mind create emotional states and subsequent behaviors. We are not readily aware of our created behaviors either. Most of the time, we are probably not even aware that we are acting unconsciously, or even stated more appropriately, just *reacting*. Scientists, and especially neuroscientists, state that we use but 10% to 20% of our brain capacity and they hunger for ways to increase this percentage. They falsely assume that the brain and the mind are one and that if we can use more neural circuits we will somehow improve the mind. Close examination in real life shows the majority of our behavior is controlled by the unconscious mind—that is, the programs generated by our conditioning. So, it is not necessarily clear that efforts to increase use of more brain circuits will improve our life, beyond perhaps having increased long-term memory capability. It is our emotions, and our behaviors as dictated from these emotions—that is the fabric of our lives.

**Emotions give us the juice of living—propelling us forward, enhancing our quality of living.**

The conscious mind acts in a relatively slow manner. The subconscious mind acts extremely rapidly, perhaps millions of times faster than the conscious mind. Thus, our decisions, behavior, and the ensuing actions can turn out to be beyond our conscious awareness. That is, until the consequence of the action emerges. Most of these behaviors arise from these conditioning programs, which have been running in the background for many years and will continue to run—as they are ever ready to spring into action.

**Remember, the conscious mind is the logical linear reasoned mind (i.e., the thinking mind).** The conscious mind primarily functions with self-dialogue asking questions and by retrieving stored experiential data. However, it is not readily provable that the resulting decisions from thinking are produced in or by the conscious mind, since most of our behaviors and our actions result from our unconscious programs.

Importantly, these subconscious programs operate in such a manner that they will interpret, or filter information in a way that validates these programs as authentic. These programs can be understood better as sets of internal instructions; the "ought tos," and the "shoulds," and "you must do this," and "you must not do that," and "as a good boy (girl), that is wrong." Sadly, the vast majority of our conditioned programing is not positively reinforcing programming, but negative.

As an example, take something simple like the fact that all of us were raised—that is, *programmed*—to not talk to strangers. As a child we may accept this despite it seeming natural to speak with someone. Then, as a 20-, 30-, or 40-year-old adult, when we meet a stranger as we are walking down the street, the programming kicks into gear. It is not our conscious mind that is thinking or evaluating or analyzing. It is not the conscious mind saying, by internal dialogue, *"Let us look at this person and evaluate their clothing, let us evaluate their facial expression, let us evaluate their height, their weight, their posture, whether they are smiling, or what are they expressing."* No, the conditioned program is running quickly ahead of any conscious considerations, and it is controlling our behavior: the dominant message is, *don't talk to strangers.*

Since our conditioning from our birth forward is overwhelmingly negative, it is entirely accurate to assume that these programs, all of which operate without our conscious awareness, may not provide us with the best paths or options in our lives.

Another example has to do with speaking up. Perhaps,

while growing up, every time that we attempted to ex-press ourselves openly—to speak what we were think-ing, in some situation—we would get a stern look from a parent, a stern look from a teacher, or even their words that would stop us from freely expressing our opinion. If this happened enough times (or maybe it just happened once with intensity), the programming becomes deeply embedded in our subconscious: *it is not good to speak out and give our view.* Now, when you are 20, 30, or 40 years old and you are in a relationship (with family, friends, or colleagues) where it is necessary to express yourself, there is this controlling program in your subconscious dictat-ing, *"do not speak up."* It may not even coming into your consciousness—it is just there and you are unaware—and this is what might be directing you in some particular life situation , and not your conscious mind, not your clever thinking mind. Your logical, linear mind with its vast data memory may not even be at work here.

Yes, you want to say something, give your thoughts and opinions, but this unconscious programming is there and, being fast and sufficiently strong, it is going to take control in the situation. You may not even be aware that this program is there. Instead, you may simply think of yourself as shy, and, your not wanting to express your-self is maybe who you think you are. You are just "natu-rally" shy. This is untrue. The conditioning program was put in there, not by you but by your mother, father, teach-er, preacher, peers, and/or your culture—and it will take control. The subconscious programming has the power to rule without the conscious mind even being aware of it.

So, here, anxiety can be experienced. It is experienced by your body, with a specific pattern within the entirety of your body. To have anxiety means that there is apprehension or fear. In this situation—a subconscious program is preventing you from speaking up, even perhaps knowing that you do want to speak. Conflict arises and there is fear in this conflict. This resultant fear is called anxiety.

## Conclusion

The mind is certainly part of the problem's configuration. It is not the only part. Nonetheless, in having a conscious mind, we do have a certain capability to make good use of it in finding an inventive ways for looking at the problem. The challenge is using the conscious mind in a new way, as a "junior partner," in finding genuine solutions for dissolving anxiety without the conscious mind taking control. There is the conscious mind's old way— that belief that we can *just think* our way through anxiety. This old way is comforting because of our conditioning that our mind and reasoning is the end all. For the most part, this is not true.

A better approach is to use the mind in a skilled and clever way toward accomplishing our end, which is finding real solutions to anxiety and removing it from our lives—something that is certainly possible.

# Chapter 4
# **The Body**

We are given but one body to sustain us during our journey in this world—and our bodies are sensitive and perceptive to a wide array of input, be it food or experiences, and the feelings accompanying those experiences. Emotions reside in our bodies and influence our health and, essentially, the body's function. This chapter explains how emotions are experienced *in* the body and the effect on us—and even how, in a very unique way, we can ask questions and have the body respond directly to get candid, correct answers. We can use the body as a tool in solving the problem of our anxiety.

## **Adored, Neglected, and Unaware—All at the Same Time**

There seems to be a paradox regarding our bodies. We really love our outer shell, but know very little about the entirety of our body, or its intricate complexity. In most cultures, a tremendous amount of value is placed on physical appearance. We place value on the hair, desiring it be in proper places like on top of the head—a full head of hair is esteemed—but certainly not on our legs or arms if we are female. We place value on the skin being clear as well as lighter or darker, depending on the culture. We place value on the shape and size of the body. We are obsessed with weight. In most cultures, it is preferred that the male body is larger rather than smaller; a man's body is more appreciated if it is more muscular and not fat.

For women, there are almost innumerable preferences regarding every facet of their body. In Western culture, we literally spend billions—perhaps hundreds of billions—of dollars on our physical appearances. We place tremendous value on a youthful appearance versus an aged appearance, and we go to great lengths to maintain a youthful appearance.

It is interesting that when one person describes another (in most all cultures), they do so by first mentioning a physical attribute: tall or short, heavy or thin, something regarding their hair or skin. The description usually mentions whether they look attractive or unattractive, if they are beautiful or not beautiful, if they are handsome or not

Occasionally, a person may be described in a different manner—by wealth, by stature, notoriety, or even intelligence—but generally this is the exception. Even so, if the description is about nonphysical attributes, it may be assumed that the described person probably has something physically not pleasing about them. Descriptors like, "She really has a nice personality" or, "He is a very thoughtful person," sometimes sets off an alarm—they must look really bad. Most people are not initially described relative to their emotional state or their moral character. This concept of the body and the physical appearance is one that is quite strong in our culture and, in fact, in most cultures.

## Food Is Mood

Three times a day (or more) we pay attention to our body by supplying it with food and what should really be called fuel. Our attention to supplying the body with food as fuel is centered on building and rebuilding our internal structure and energy for activity. However, food can and does affect our emotional state of being. It is often used even daily to alter our state of mind. **Beyond sustenance, food is mood**.

When we intake food, whether it be sugars, proteins, fats, natural substances like caffeine, or so many other naturally occurring substances ,the body's biochemistry is instantly altered. These foods alter mood by elevating a variety of hormones, leading the person to feel full for sure, and probably energized, wired, or maybe *numbed*. Sometimes we use these to excess, especially sugar, caffeine, or fats. When we eat a high carbohydrate meal (or simple sugars), both insulin and adrenalin are released quickly, producing a pseudo-energized and even motivated state. This also happens with caffeine or caffeine-like substances. We feel buzzed and ready to "get it going." A meal with high fat content creates a sense of fullness, you feel satiated, and of course when we feel full, we feel good.

So, in addition to placing great value on our appearance, we self-regulate our feelings by the direct use of food, with its immediate effect on the body, because this is precisely where emotions reside. As addressed in Chapter 2, emotions are in the body. When food is taken in, mood is generated—like it or not. As we said before, emotions dwell in the body.

Knowing that eating something alters our body, our body's biochemistry, and our body's function, we are creating, enhancing, or diminishing some emotion, good or bad. When we use substances that are not necessarily food products, for example, alcohol, drugs, cigarettes (not things that are necessarily nutritious), these too alter our state of emotional being. So food directly affects the body, thus creating emotion. Food tends to move us to the right in a representational model of our emotional continuum. Since emotions are of the body, the resulting emotion from food is similar to that as if that emotion occurred when we held a good or positive thought.

However, in using food to alter our emotional state, akin to drugs, the obvious problem is that which takes us in one direction, in the end, will also then move us in the opposite direction. If we have something that takes us up, for sure we are going to be crashing down afterward. It does not make a difference whether that something is a natural food, or especially something unnatural like stimulants, drugs, alcohol, and cigarettes. A price will be paid. We know this scientifically of course, but also from our own direct experience or our intuition.

The paradox is that we have such dedication and enthusiasm for our physical appearance, and take time and care in its upkeep, yet little appreciation for the beautiful complexity of the body—all its working systems. We are not very educated or clear about what our body's systems do or what they provide us. That is until we have a system failure, which suddenly requires our attention. In our ignorance, we intake substances that damage the inside of our bodies—something we wouldn't willingly do to the exterior.

### Emotions Imprint on Our Bodies

We live on this planet for but a brief period of time. This is living in a physical plane, and our physical being is our body. This is where our essence, our being, plays out on this planet. The body has about 3,700 trillion cells. Each one of those cells, in addition to its normal mission, also functions like a miniature battery—with a negative and a positive pole. The same is true of the body's organs, an organized collection of cells. These organs, themselves, also exhibit polarity with a positive and a negative.

There are also 100 trillion bacteria living in our intestines. We have 100 billion neurons in our bodies. We have 206 bones in our skeletal system and 642 muscles to move these bones and joints around. We have 11 organ systems with 78 organs. We have 5½ quarts of blood in our bodies, with 60 miles of vessels to move blood, transport oxygen, bring glucose to each and every cell for fuel, and then simultaneously remove carbon dioxide and the waste products from our bodies. In our blood, we have 7 or 8 million red blood cells collectively containing about 2.5 grams of iron, with another 2.5 grams of iron stored elsewhere in our bodies. The iron in our blood is necessary for the transportation of oxygen to each cell and the removal of carbon dioxide. All of this is mind boggling if we stop and think about it. We literally have billions of processes going on every second, in our cells and in our bacterial biome.

The body is magnificent. It is complex, and there seems to be nothing that has the same degree of complexity as our bodies, yet the average person knows very little about that body. We throw food (or even junk) into it, and the body transforms it into blood, muscles, and bones; each of those trillions of cells functions very systematically in a very orderly fashion. These cells function intelligently and in rhythm and in with incredible harmony, all the while working under the guidance of the unconscious mind. They do so miraculously. Incredibly, we are usually able to rebound if our body is disturbed by the conscious mind choosing to consume bad food or substances.

We are rooted in our bodies. The body supports everything that we do. When we love, the body supports us. When we hate, the body similarly supports us. When we get extremely angry, the body supports us. When we become protective, the body supports us. Whatever emotion, in every way, the body supports us. Again, emotions reside in our body, so this is no surprise. What else could the body do? It supports us in good or bad.

The body has many mysteries within it, and we certainly should not work against the body. We do not want to condemn it. This is our house that we live in. We need to respect it, we need to care about it; we actually need to love this body. We need to listen to this body. We need to talk to it. We may even need to ask it questions—there is, in fact, a very unique way to ask question and permit the body to respond accurately, which is discussed later.

Remember, **there is a connection between the mind**

**and the body—a profound connection—and that profound connection is emotion**. When a brief thought runs through our mind, or when a thought is held, there is an emotional response. There is no maybe, no perhaps, no possibly here. That response is the associated emotion that arises in the entirety of our body—every cell, every organ, every system. An emotional pattern is imprinted here upon our body. This body imprint can be thought of as an exhibited pattern resulting from an array of settings— perhaps billions of "settings" of our cells, organs, and systems.

All of us can look at another person, and unconsciously (or perhaps even consciously) distinguish their state of being almost instantly. We can sense if they are annoyed, if they are sad, if they are mad, if they are in pain, if they are tense, if they are feeling anything. We can see this simply by looking and yes, by sensing. Certainly any positive emotional state of being is seen and sensed as well. If they are content. If they are happy. If they are relaxed. All of these are sensed also. We can recognize if they are amused, if they are happy, peaceful, touched, content, or if they are loving. Even if we are so into ourselves and don't know it consciously, our unconscious recognizes it. Whether they are afraid or grieving or skeptical or mad or confused, it is apparent; we are aware of the emotional pattern overlaid on that body, either consciously or unconsciously. Remember that there is one body imprint, or emotional pattern, for each specific emotion. This pattern and an array of settings are cast on and within the body, therein affecting all the body's systems. It affects all hormones. It affects every muscle. It affects heart, lungs, kidneys, spleen . . . each and every organ. It affects the immune system. It affects all sensory perception, enhancing some and dampening others. This pattern and settings are related to that specific emotion and are set on and within the body.

For each and any emotion that we name along our own continuum line, between loving and fearing, an emotional pattern, an array of settings, is created.

## A Wise Man, Ahead of His Time: Applied Kinesiology

In 1964, Dr. George Goodhart, a chiropractor in Detroit, Michigan, formulated a new system within the healing arts. He developed, along with some other practitioners, a system for evaluating the body's function. This system was called *Applied Kinesiology*, or AK, and it dealt with the functional health disturbances of the body as opposed to pathology of the body. Pathology is the state of a tissue in disease and can be evaluated, in the ultimate sense, histologically or in a cadaver at autopsy. Functional disturbances are not detected in the same way. In AK, the physician uses the patient's body itself as an investigating tool and in treatment as well. AK evaluates functional disturbances, but is keen to detect disease.

AK looks at an individual in terms of the triad of health: structure (the muscles and joints), chemistry (with food and other substances), and the mental or psychological aspects of our bodies. This is the considered triad of health.

As a fundamental tool, and method of inquiry, AK uses muscles and muscle testing when asking questions permitting the body to respond candidly. The basic belief of AK is that the body never lies; you only need to ask a viable question and the body truthfully reacts. This reaction or response can be evaluated with muscle testing. The unconscious mind (with its unifying influence throughout the entirety of the body) better reflects the truth. The body simply acknowledges and responds what is asked, without prejudice, judgment, clever analysis, or assessment. If we are simply questioned, the conscious mind instantly begins thousands of evaluations based on our preconceived ideas and filters all possible responses in or for preservation of the ego. Here the response is probably not the truth or the reality of the situation, but a response that protects the ego. However, when we ask the body a question, the body will give an unfiltered answer. It responds to what is—not what could be, what should be, what might be, what's possible, what's in it for me, which would be the mind and ego questioning. Using muscle testing, we can ask the subconsciously controlled body a question. The body will give us the authentic, valued answer. It is independent of the mind.

If we simply ask, for example, "Are you happy today?" the conscious mind's response will attempt to evaluate why you are asking the question—is it good to answer it, is it good or safe to answer it truthfully, should your feelings be kept hidden? There are plenty of questions and internal evaluations that the mind is going to ask before it gives a conscious reply, and that is not necessarily going to be the truth.

If the body is asked a question, such as, "Are you happy today?" and the response is evaluated through muscle testing, then we are going to get an answer that is reflective of the truth because the emotion happy resides in the body. If indeed you are happy, you are going to have that emotional pattern, or imprint, in the body that is happiness. The muscle will test strong in accord with the truth; and, if not, then the muscle will test weak.

Parts of Applied Kinesiology, and some of the techniques and treating methods using this philosophy, were the basis for the beginning of the field of Energy Psychology. These procedures were expanded upon in the mid-1980s. Many times after a patient issues were tackled by attention directed at the first two parts of health triad, there remained some pain or dysfunction. Dr. Goodheart and his colleagues recognized an acu-point approach for dissolving the final emotional part of the problem. This is elaborated and discussed in Chapter 8, while investigating radical approaches for removing ourselves from an anxious state.

## Conclusion

### Key Points to Remember:

- While we groom and beautify the body, we both have a poor understanding of how incredible it is and, in doing so, neglect it as well. Its function is ignored until there is dysfunction.

- The body is incredibly complex, magnificent, and wonderful in its function. There is nothing equivalent to its coordinated majesty of function.

- The significance of the body as part of the structure of the problem is that the emotion anxiety is a physiological pattern and an array of settings, which is imprinted on and within the body.

- Applied Kinesiology values the emotional truth, which is found in the body. It uses muscle testing to evaluate responses to appropriate questions.

- Applied Kinesiology investigated approaches and developed methods for evaluating emotional issues. Initially, this was done to correct the emotional component of a pain or functional problem.

- Energy Psychology uses Applied Kinesiology as a component in the basis of its fundamental methods.

# Chapter 5
# Energy

The third and final piece of the structure of our problem of anxiety is the energy systems of our body. It was understandable when we spoke about mind and body being part of the structure because, when we are anxious we are thinking about something (the mind), and we feel it in our body with tension, sweat, and maybe a quickened pulse (the body). Now, we look at this (perhaps new age) concept of the energy systems of our body. The body's energy systems include our Aura, the Chakras, and the Meridians—which are essential to the way anxiety is experienced and imprinted in our body.

## It Is Not About Having More Red Bull

Typically, when we talk about our energy, we are referring to our ability to do something—increasing our "oomph," or our "get-up-and-go." When we wake up in the morning, is there sufficient energy for the rest of day? Will we have enough energy later or even at the end of the day to do something we want to do? Will we have energy in the afternoon to finish work after eating lunch? Will we have energy to play? This energy is more related to our metabolism and blood sugar levels, or even sleep hygiene. Although important, this chapter does not consider the energy taken from the food that we eat—that is, our metabolism—and whether or how we process refined carbohydrates (sugars) to avoid hypoglycemia and its sad or depressed association. Of course, in our modern society, when our metabolic energy fades typically we take some caffeine product to increase our chances to better perform or accomplish tasks.

In this chapter, we consider energy from a different perspective. We address our *energy systems*—more from an electromagnetic aspect—which is the third piece of the structure of the problem of anxiety. The body's energy systems include Auras, Chakras, and Meridians. These, respectively, represent places where energy exists, is stored, and the ways of which energy flows. This intermediate energy structure regarding the problem of anxiety is central, for without it there would be no ability for anxiety or any emotion to occur.

## Fields of Energy

The human body contains about 3,700 trillion cells—from the follicles of your hair, to your liver cells, to your heart cells, muscle cells, and nerve cells. Along with performing their normal functions, each cell, every single one of them, is also like a miniature battery. Thus, they all have an electric charge associated with them. They have polarity: a positive pole and a negative pole. These cells are also in constant motion; you are not a statue and even if we are completely still, or think we are, there is always movement. Even when we are sleeping, there is move-

PART TWO THE PROBLEM STRUCTURE

ment of our body, there is movement of organs, and there is a constant flow in our body. Nothing is stagnant. We know from physics that everything that has a charge to it also has an electric field. So, we have 3,700 trillion cells that are charged, and each of them has an electric field. This is not even including the 100 or so billion of bacteria that populate us. Even though each cell's electrical charge is infinitesimally small, the total collective charge is not insignificant.

If we look at organs, which are comprised of organized packed cells—for example, the brain, the heart, the liver, the kidney, etc.—they have a considerable amount of electric charge that is easily measureable. We are all familiar with an electrocardiogram machine (EKG), whose purpose is to measure our heart's electrical activity. After being hooked up with 5 to 12 electrodes on your torso, you can watch this electrical activity on a screen, or get a paper printout. You can see the electrical phenomena that make the heart contract and relax. The heart even has its own electrical wiring system along with the millions of cells that comprise the heart's overall charge.

We can similarly look at the brain. Within this compact clump of gray and white matter are about 100 billion neurons. This is a staggering number. Every single neuron of the brain functions in sending or transferring signals and information by creating a change of polarity (plus and minus), as the outside of the cell changes from positive to negative, creating a flow of this charge. We can see this brain activity with an EEG (electroencephalography) machine with electrodes placed on our skull, and recording the activity on a screen similar to the heart's EKG mentioned before. The EEG can also be shown on something like a mini TV where different patterns or, more precisely, different waves representing the electrical activity of or in the brain are demonstrated. There is a continuous and varied rhythm of electrical charge. These can be printed out on long rolls of chart paper for interpretation.

This electric field that is associated with every single cell radiates out spherically from that cell in every direction. Collectively, if we look at the entire body, with trillions of cells, there is an electric field radiating out from the body—it is moving through the body and away from the body.

Additionally, our bodies have a magnetic field as well. Where does this come from? First, you have red blood cells, which contain iron. We have about 2.5 grams of this iron collectively in 7 or 8 million blood cells. So we have iron, a conductor, moving through the electric field of the body. This creates magnetism, as we know from physics: if you have a conductor moving through an electric field, you have a magnetic field created. Similarly, if you have an electric field that itself is moving and changing through something that a conductor, like iron, a magnetic field is created.

Additionally, most molecules themselves can generate their own small magnetic field. Imagine the simple experiment we have often seen as children: take a little bar magnet with a south and north pole, hold it underneath a piece of paper on which you've sprinkled little iron filings, and we readily see that it has an invisible field demonstrated by fine iron lines on our paper going out from one pole to another.

We all have heard of Magnetic Resonance Imaging, or an MRI. Magnetic resonance works when we place our body inside this powerful electromagnetic tube. When a strong magnetic field is applied, it acts on the water molecules in our body. Each molecule contains the positive protons, and protons themselves behave like little moving magnets. When our body is subjected to a powerful magnetic field, these protons line up in the same direction, much in the same way that a magnet can pull the needle of a compass. Radio waves (electric field) are then applied, and these electric fields knock these protons (the little magnets), out of alignment. Then the radio waves are turned off and the protons, these little magnets, realign. When this happens, the protons send out electrical signals that are picked up by the receivers. This is seen on a detector and, like magic, an image is created. This is what we then see.

The bottom line is that we have a variety of magnetic fields within the body—from the water in the body, macromolecules, and from iron and other elements within the body. This magnetic field interacts with all the electrons in the body, so you have this constant flow of electricity, and magnetism. We are all energy, and this energy is electromagnetic energy, which is comprised of both electric fields and magnetic fields.

## Your Aura: The Radiance of Your Life Energy

We can look at this electric and magnetic field activity in totality and this energy field represents and reflects everything that is happening within the body. When viewed from this overall perspective, it is called the *biological field*, *biofield*, or the *Aura*. A lot of healers have the ability to actually see another person's Aura. In the past, some Russian and Japanese photographers succeeded at taking images of the Aura. Similarly, many Japanese researchers have imaged the Aura of other living things, like plants.

We are glowing, perhaps not like a 200-watt incandescent light bulb, but nonetheless an electromagnetic energy field radiates from our being. We have the ability actually to feel this Aura. We start by rubbing our hands together, get them very warm, and then very softly put our hands about 6 inches apart, shut our eyes, and slowly bring our hands together. As we bring our hands together, we are going to start to feel something strange happening between them. Some people describe this as a tingling, some people describe it as warmth, but when we start to feel this sensation, that is the Aura, our biofield, and we are using our hands for detection. We can use this to sense the rest of our body's Aura or even others' Auras. We can place our hands close to our face, or close to our leg, and we can sense the Aura. With simple practice and sensitivity, we can start sensing this in other people as well. This is the first of our energy systems described in this chapter, and it is seen in Illustration 5.

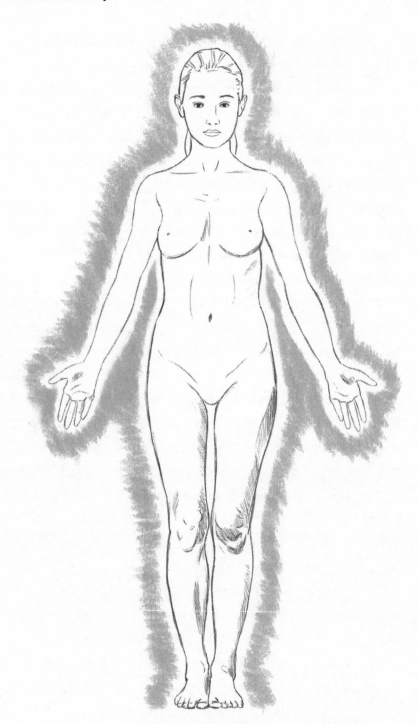

Illustration 5: The Aura.

This is the radiance of the energy of life—and bear in mind that energy comes about at the moment of our inception and leaves at the moment of our demise—and within our body system it is electromagnetic energy. This energy is actually measurable with electric field meters and magnetometers that read our electric and magnetic fields, respectively. It is subtle, it is small, but it is measurable.

## The Chakras: Where Energy Is Stored

We have all this energy and since it not used up instantly, it needs some placed to be stored so that it is available when we need it. How is this energy of life stored in our body, if it is truly stored? This question is answered by a centuries' old notion of whirling vortices or "generators" of energy that have the ability to speed up (thus having more energy within them) or slow down (resulting in less energy within them). These vortices or generators were named Chakras.

The concept of Chakras is a very old one. The concept comes from Indian tradition, around 2000 or 3000 years BC. The word *Chakra* itself means a disk or a wheel. They were first mentioned in the Vedas, or the Hindu texts, and it has even been written that they may have come from an Aryan culture that preceded the Indian Hindu culture by several generations (many centuries).

The Chakras act as both storehouses and transporters of our universal life energy, and the Chakras are indispensable with regard to our energy flow. There are many excellent books written about Chakras. Each Chakra itself is associated with a certain part of the body. It is generally agreed that there are seven Chakras, as shown in Illustration 6.

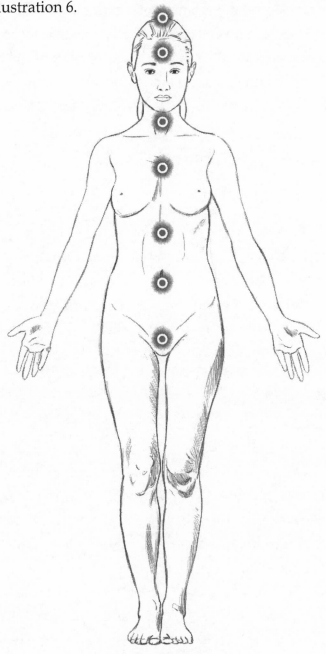

Illustration 6: The Chakras.

The Chakras have Sanskrit, or Hindi names, and together with their assigned body areas, there are many different specific qualities related to each Chakra. The **first Chakra** (root Chakra) is at the very base of your spine or at the very bottom on your groin. The **second Chakra** (sacral or spleen Chakra) is located just a few inches above that, below the belly button. The **third Chakra** (stomach or solar plexus Chakra) is in the middle at the belly button. The **fourth Chakra**, the heart Chakra, is centered on the heart. The **fifth Chakra** (throat Chakra) is at the throat. The **sixth Chakra** (brow or pineal Chakra) is between your eyes, and the **seventh Chakra** (crown Chakra) is at the crown, or top vertex, of your head. These whirling vortices of energy are located on or about the body—or, more accurately, *through* the body. Also, traditionally, various glands and organs are associated with each Chakra.

In terms of the specific attributes mentioned above, the first Chakra is associated with the sexual organs themselves and the second Chakra specifically with the ovaries or the testicles. The third Chakra is associated with the adrenals and the pancreas. The fourth Chakra is associated with the thymus. The fifth Chakra is associated with the thyroid and the parathyroid. The sixth Chakra is associated with the pineal gland, and the seventh Chakra is associated with the pituitary gland.

Similarly, for each Chakra, there is an associated color, smells, sounds, tastes, frequencies, foods, and addictions. Most importantly, there are mental or emotional aspects associated with each Chakra.

For our purpose here, the emotional correlations are

crucial. Emotionally, the first Chakra, the root Chakra, is associated with our actual desire to be alive, our willingness to exist on this earth. It has to do with our willingness to procreate. The second Chakra, which is the spleen Chakra, is associated with our emotional intensity. It has to do with our personal warmth, our intimacy, our pleasure, our joy. The third Chakra, the solar plexus Chakra, is associated with our mental vitality and strength—our thinking, our beliefs, our control, and our details about life. It has to do with our perfection. How are good things getting done?

The fourth Chakra, the heart Chakra, obviously has to do with lovingness, with harmony and trust, and the ability to give and receive. The fifth Chakra, the throat Chakra, has to do with communication, with speaking what we think and with creativity, speaking up, and breathing. The sixth Chakra is the brow Chakra, and this Chakra has to do with our ability to see things overall—to actually visualize things, to see choices, to see that things are cohesive. The last Chakra, the seventh Chakra (crown Chakra), has to do with our connection with something beyond ourselves, with connection with the universal—seeing ourselves as part of one.

The concept of Chakras as whirling vortices of energy and their physical, bodily associations started with healers in the past, which manipulated these Chakras. These healers diagnosed the Chakras as having too much or too little energy. Their method of treatment then involved moving energy from one Chakra to another, to produce balance and energy stability. And, in so doing, transforms both the physical and the emotional well-being of that individual.

The same concept of producing balance and equilibrium could apply to any healer working with a person's aforementioned Aura. Energy is transferred from areas of excess to areas of deficiency. So the effort is to attune the Aura to gain emotional balance and harmony consistent for physical and mental health of that individual.

## The Meridians: Where Energy Moves

The third, and last, discussion about energy is related to the flow of energy—the flow of the life energy as it moves through us. This is the energy that was given to us at conception; we have all of this life energy called *qi* or *chi*, which was given to us at creation. We know that as we inhale, we intake energy called *qi* or *pranna*; as we exhale, energy leaves us. We know that as we bring food and water into our bodies, we bring *qi* energy into us, and as we excrete, energy leaves us. These are certainly the ingredients needed to sustain life energy. There is an ebb and flow, and waves of energy are continuous as we live.

As stated previously, we have Chakras (these whirlpools) within which energy is stored—some Chakras may have excess, some Chakras may be deficient. When they have too much or too little energy, a disruption occurs in the person's physical and emotional well-being. Whatever the situation, this energy must move, and avoid stagnation, so the last thing to address is how energy flows within the body. Balance is needed, not only regarding

Chakras that store this energy, but in energy flow. We turn to Traditional Chinese Medicine (TCM) for this.

TCM considers life energy, which they call *chi* or *qi*, as flowing through the body in various channels. The channels are also called *Meridians*, or channels (both used interchangeably in this text). Primarily, there are 12 paired Meridians. Conceptually similar to Chakras, these 12 Meridians have associated organs in the body. Additionally there is also a Meridian that runs down the front of the body and another that runs down the back of the body, as seen in Illustration 7. So, in total, there are 14 Meridians.

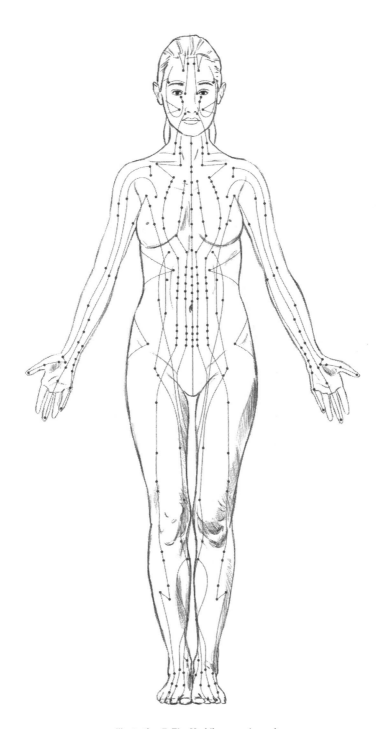

Illustration 7: The Meridians, or channels.

PART TWO THE PROBLEM STRUCTURE

Each of the 12 paired Meridians is associated with an organ, and the organ is either thought of as solid, which would be *yin*, or hollow, which would be *yang*. The fundamental concept in TCM is one of polarity; the energy within us is both positive and negative—*yang and yin*, respectively. The treating principle of TCM is to create a balance of yin and yang.

The understanding is that there is a flow of energy from one Meridian to another, to another, to another, as energy courses through the entire body. This is the movement of *qi*. TCM says that when the flow is disrupted, such that there could be piling up of energy or alternatively a deficiency of energy at an area or point on along a particular Meridian, then dysfunction or disease occurs. This disruption can cause an increase or decrease in the overall energy within Meridian.

Along each Meridian are various points that are associated with different physical things; there are close to a thousand different points. In TCM, the most sensitive points are at the beginnings and ends of Meridians; there are also specific points that connect one Meridian to another, and there are master points where one Meridian can control another Meridian. Acupuncture therapy and treatment involves treating these points with the overall emphasis to re-create balance and harmony. However, it should be noted that TCM is not one single codified approach or recipe but, rather, experientially derived approaches from hundreds of different ancestry of therapists, of acupuncturists, each with their own experiential methods of treatment. Beyond balance, the important concept of TCM is that energy must freely flow.

Life energy moves through the body. There is even research that demonstrates this. Japanese researchers put ions (charged particles) near particular acupoints of the body and then watched if or how these ions might move. What they saw was movement independent of the blood flow of the body. It is also independent of the nervous system, of the nerve paths that run through the body. It was independent of the lymphatic flow of the body, the part of our circulatory system that carries this fluid, called *lymph*, back toward the heart. This important lymph system gets plasma back from our tissues and returns it to the blood. Another function of the lymph system is that it carries white blood cells and things called *lymphocytes*. Thus, this independent flow of ions provides some modern verification of the TCM channels of energy.

### Meridians and Emotions

By experience, certain emotions are associated with very specific Meridians. Worry (or excessive strained mental activity) is associated with the spleen channel (SP) and perhaps the stomach Meridian (ST), which is a paired Meridian. The emotions of grief and sadness, especially sadness, are associated with the lung Meridian (LU) and its paired Meridian, the large intestine channel (LI). The emotions of frustration and irritability and anger are associated with the liver Meridian (LR) and its paired Meridian, the gallbladder channel (GB). The emotion of fear and of being insecure is associated with the kidney channel (KI) and its associated Meridian, the bladder Meridian (BL).

In TCM, when treating someone for an emotional issue, we look at the Meridian associated with that particular emotion, trying to discover whether it is in excess or is deficient. Then, the particular treatment is directed at moving energies from one Meridian to another, seeking balance.

## Conclusion

These three energy systems—the Aura, the Chakras, and now the Meridians—are the basis on which our solution is focused (as addressed in Chapters 9 and 10). The mind and body are not dismissed in our solution, but they are used creatively but simply as an adjunct.

Anxiety, or really the problem of anxiety as a state of being, is related to the mind (a held thought) and the body (where emotion dwells). We've now outlined and described the body's energy systems. Thus, the problem of anxiety is structured in the mind, body, and energy systems of the body. The chapters of Part Three examine how different past and newer approaches offer solutions using these three components—either individually or collectively.

# PART THREE
# THE PROBLEM'S SOLUTIONS

Anxiety is the problem and, thus far, we have addressed how that problem arises from and affects the mind, the body, and the energy systems—where the problem of anxiety is structured. Given this, we could look at solving the problem by only looking at the mind (which has been the traditional approach), by looking at the body only (and some past and current solutions have centered around this exclusively), or by looking solely at the body's energy systems (which is a "new," emerging approach over the last 15 to 20 years). Historically, there have been many healers that exclusively employ energy techniques by themselves to treat emotional issues like anxiety. In reality, there are many that continue to do so currently.

Anxiety was, has been, and is an issue. What's been tried before? What's new? What are radical or outrageous approaches in addressing anxiety?

Any person with a personal problem or an issue such as anxiety certainly wants to fix it, and there is no lack of approaches. There are new adaptations and modifications and restructuring of traditional methods, and some of these are briefly outlined in Chapters 6 and 7, but simply as a foundation for enhanced understanding.

We also focus some unique methods in Chapter 8 that rely exclusively on the body itself to solve the challenge of anxiety. A radical new approach called *Energy Psychology* is discussed, enhancing our groundwork. Then, in Chapter 9, a totally outrageous process called REIN, which stands for *Resolving Emotional Issues Now*, is presented. REIN is a fusion of many methods. The REIN process provides a step-by-step method for dissolving anxiety. REIN is an approach that can be implemented now, and its efficacy can similarly be measured immediately.

In Part Two, we looked at how the problem is structured in the mind and the body with respect to our energy fields. Now, we proceed in a manner that methodically looks at how an individual having anxiety might approach a sensible resolution.

Our examination of traditional approaches and even newer, radical approaches is not meant to be a comprehensive list, nor is it meant to be a detailed and precise examination of every method that is enumerated in the following chapters. It is not about comparing and contrasting approaches. Rather, the review provides background and greater understanding for us to appreciate the **value of an integrated approach,** like REIN. The greater our understanding, with more perceived richness, the better chance for successfully using this REIN approach. It would not be sufficient to just list the seven steps of REIN and assume it can be accurately followed. It is necessary to first define the problem of anxiety and then examine anxiety's framework. And now, it is valuable as well as instructive to look at other prior approaches for evaluation and inclusion of their best aspects.

# Chapter 6
# **Traditional Approaches**

In attacking the problem of anxiety—our enemy, so to speak—we can use a simplified analogy of attacking this enemy with various weaponry available to us. This chapter lightly surveys some traditional methods people have sought in the past and currently often seek for solving the problem of anxiety.

## Where Do We Look for Help?

We seem to be constantly challenged with anxiety, stress, and fear. What to do? Reasonably functioning human beings, like most organisms, have a desire to move more to what they think as a positive direction and away from things that are negative. Inherent in our non-conscious being is to avoid that which will injure or destroy us. It is natural. It is meant for survival. It is innate within all of us. However, we do not want to live in anxiety of anticipated fear every waking second. Since our conditioning moves us away from the present moment, from the here and now, and into the future of *what ifs*, we suffer much constant anxiety. Most of us, when anxiety is at hand, want to try to resolve that anxiety in some way that would move us in a positive direction.

Given that we have developed this amazing ability to think, to process information, and to examine and review our past decisions, we can use our conscious mind with our faculties to then ask questions to ourselves. This seems to almost define the process of thinking itself: namely, asking questions.

So, it makes sense that the first thing we are going to do regarding anxiety is to actually try to think our own way through it. If we are confused and unfocused, this is what we attempt. And if we were unable to think it through ourselves, most of us would talk with friends or colleagues or relatives or parents or children in order to try to remedy the situation. We would talk and think, challenging the conscious mind to solve our issue of constant anxiety that we believe relates to the mind.

When it does not get solved to our satisfaction, perhaps then we might try finding a minister or a priest or a rabbi, and see if we can find assistance and gain some insight or clarity for the solution of our anxiety.

All of this supposes that we are aware that there is an issue and that we choose to do something about it. It is entirely possible we may feel constant discontent without our even recognizing what is really happening. Conversely, we may feel anxiety, yet assume it is part of life that is shared with everyone—the status quo—so, if we feel anxious and are satisfied existing in that state of anxiety, then that is fine, we can choose to do that. There is no law, there is no dictate, there is no mandate that we live our life in any particular emotional state. It is entirely up to us.

Perhaps if we are aware that our emotional state of

being is currently anxiety, and it is preventing us from doing what we want to do, we can take action. We may seek counseling with a licensed clinical social worker, psychologist, counselor, or a life coach—somebody of that ilk. There are a variety of different professionals from which we can choose. Prior to that we may have used a medical model and sought out a physician and/or a psychiatrist to get medication to reduce our anxiety. Sadly, many people take this route. Anxiety medications are the second most prescribed medication type in the United States and account for tens of billions of dollars of pharmaceutical sales every year. However, even before trying that path, we may have tried to self-medicate with food or with alcohol or with illicit drugs to diminish our anxiety so that we might function more resourcefully. This is quite common—to keep masking, blocking, and denying anxiety in the hope it will fade. It does not.

If we did not elect the medical model, as said before, we may have sought out a professional therapist. Therapists have a common thread amongst all of them—and that is the use of talking, thinking, and communication. These are essential in the therapeutic process between client and therapist. The therapy's implicit goal is for us to be able to gain insight and thereby develop new strategies to "deal" with anxiety, or to "cope" with anxiety. Therapy in general, as well as counseling, tries to create a nice environment that is free and secure from distraction and enables us, the client, to speak freely and to open up discussing all aspects of our anxiety. This is about thinking, talking, analyzing (questions), and looking at different strategies. This is a mind-centered approach in looking for solutions.

A therapist may use a variety of methods to try to persuade us to change the direction that we have chosen. If we have decided that anxiety is an issue and we want to be less anxious, then the therapist is going to choose different techniques toward that goal, but the treatment approach is certainly based upon thinking. Approaches are centered on both dialog and the relationship between the therapist and the client, and it is about exposing and correcting our "stinking thinking." It is related to the mind, the conscious mind. We are attempting to expand and improve our thinking, get better perspective, and find new insightful strategies for solving our anxiety. Both, explicitly and implicitly, the understanding is that the therapist is going to facilitate the process by which we gain this improved insight and find the root cause—that is the **why, why, why.** Traditionally the finding of the "why" is needed before real progress can be achieved. If the "why" can't be found, all paths forward are blocked. This is fundamental to the majority of approaches in therapy.

## Psychoanalysis

Psychoanalysis is the first example of talk therapy—in fact, it is considered the mother of psychotherapy. Almost everyone is familiar with Sigmund Freud and his development of psychoanalysis, and the three parts of our subconscious being: the id, the ego, and the superego. He thought longstanding problems were situated under the unconscious mind and related to conflicts between these three aspects. The fundamental method in psychoanalysis is the therapist–client's discussion of the patient's thoughts, fantasies, and dreams, which need to be brought forth from the subconscious mind and scrutinized and investigated. Psychoanalysis believes that problems are rooted in the conflicts of the subconscious mind and bringing them to the forefront of the conscious mind will aid in "curing" us. Psychoanalysis presumes that issues are created in the subconscious by unresolved conflict (at the first beginning of a potential problem) or by repressed past trauma of early childhood.

Then, the psychoanalyst looks to where the unconscious conflicts are creating the client's dilemma, although their interest is not in addressing behavioral problems per se. They do so with a variety of tools like ink blot tests and free association. There is an abundance of sessions of analysis! Even on a daily basis. People who enter into psychoanalysis tend to do so typically for many, many years, at significant cost. It seems to be an appropriate approach for the wealthy, or really self-absorbed, and for someone who loves to indulge in endless analysis. One might ask if "analysis" itself is the result the client is seeking.

## Gestalt Therapy

*Gestalt therapy* was developed by Freud's protégée Fritz Perls who considered that the brain sees the whole in its entirety rather than in its parts; he believed this is most evident with vision, albeit the other four senses would be included as well. One experiences things as a whole, and the whole is much more than the sum of its parts—that is, $1 + 1 + 1 + 1 + 1 + 1 + 1 \ldots$ might equal 73, not simply 7.

This therapy focuses on the here-and-now and not so much the past. It looks at what is being experienced *now*. This led to those practicing gestalt to actually incorporate Buddha's ideas of awareness. Gestalt therapists were also the first to examine the "psychology" of the *process* of problem solving itself by humans. It is a novel approach that considers the person as a whole, discusses personal responsibility, is concerned with the here-and-now, and takes a different perspective. It does not look at the unknown or the unknowable, but it looks at what is happening in the present so that the client can overcome their particular symptoms. It looks at what is thought, felt, and acted upon in this moment—not on what could or should be done. It is not about interpretation to find the "real" meaning. If they overcome those symptoms, like anxiety, they can be a whole being, alive, and especially creative in finding solutions therein and gaining freedom. While gestalt certainly takes a different perspective and is sort of an overhaul of psychoanalysis, it still relies on the same clinical framework of the therapist and client together as being essential—and, as gestalt is still based upon thinking, the mind is therefore central to the solution.

## Positive Psychotherapy

The concept of *positive psychotherapy*, in addition to treating the individual symptoms, focuses on reinforcing the positive resources of the client as character strengths. The meaning behind this—accentuating the positive resources—serves the client well in that better thinking and analysis will prevail, and a clever strategy will bubble up to resolve the issue. Here, the therapist wants to engage the client in discussions regarding their symptoms, while simultaneously paying attention to the client's other positive aspects. The assumption is that, to be effective in this therapeutic relationship so that the client can solve their problem, there has to be dialogue while at the same time emphasis and awareness of the positive resources of the individual aspect of the client. As you might imagine, this is also a lengthy process, something that requires months and months, or even years and years, of work with a therapist

## Cognitive Psychotherapy

*Cognitive psychotherapy* blossomed in the 1960s, and it is based on the idea that *how we feel is determined by how we think*. Disorders or dysfunction are a result of faulty thoughts and beliefs. So, in order to correct disorders such as sadness, depression, anxiety, anger, fear, or whatever, a change must occur in the client's perception of events: get them thinking correctly, get them thinking wisely, and the emotional state will improve. It is all about cognitive

errors—cognitive simply means thinking. We have "stinking thinking," but when we correct our "stinking thinking" with this approach, the stuck emotional state of being, like anxiety, should go away. Again, therapists work
together with their clients over weeks, months, or years,
working to point out and challenge their thinking errors
and present different ways to view the situation. In doing
so, the mood or the emotional state of being is supposedly
modified.

## Cognitive Behavioral Therapy

Cognitive behavioral therapy (CBT) is another form
of treatment that focuses on the relationship between
thoughts and feelings and behaviors. CBT is somewhat
different than traditional types of psychodynamic therapy
in that the client and the therapist work together (rather
than therapist-directed), and the treatment focuses on the
client's thought "patterns" that create behavioral issues.
The client presents with a behavioral issue that they wish
to avoid or release. During the session and afterward, the
client is encouraged to write their thoughts down as they
come, and then the therapist searches for the *patterns* in
their thinking—their "stinking thinking" *patterns*—that
causes them to have a negative perception that leads to
negative feelings which then leads to self-destructive behaviors. The concept is thoughts generate and feelings
generate behaviors, which is certainly a reasonable concept. CBT is practiced by many therapists, and today it is
used as the first line of therapy (besides and with medica-

tion) for treating anxiety disorders as well as posttraumatic stress, obsessive-compulsive, and panic disorders.

## Humanistic Psychotherapy

Humanistic psychotherapy looks at individuals based on their fundamental needs, as determined by Abraham Maslow's hierarchy of needs. Maslow was concerned about the "healthy" development of the individual and proposed that this development was based on meeting five needs, in order these are (1) physical needs, (2) safety, (3) loving & belonging, (4) esteem, and (5) self-actualization. If the needs at the fundamental first level are not fulfilled, there is *tension* and *anxiety*. This *anxiety* is actually considered a driving force. If the needs at one level are met, then person can progress toward higher needs, all the way to the last needs—that of self-actualization (i.e., what you *may be and can be*).

It is still a client-centered approach; certainly necessitating building a relationship between the client and the therapist, otherwise there is no potential for growth. Growth is determined by moving up and achieving this hierarchy of needs, which along the way does self-empower the individual, and *anxiety* is considered a necessary driving force. One of humanistic psychology's founders, Carl Rogers, focused on making sure that this developmental process, going from the lower needs to the higher needs, was a creative one. Focusing on creativity and free choice and potential, it looked at the entire person—the goal being a client with a stronger and healthier sense of

self, which would lead to what Maslow called "self-actualization."

There are some similarities between humanistic psychotherapy and gestalt therapy, which focuses on current
thoughts and feelings, the here-and-now as opposed to the
interpretation to find root causes, and the consideration
of the client as a whole. But, the humanistic psychology
therapist actively participates and creates a supportive environment where clients can establish their true identities.

## Conclusion

This is not a comprehensive list of every type of traditional approach in therapy. It is neither meant to be a
detailed view or a comparative analysis of all of these
methods of therapy but, rather, a portrayal of some different approaches that are available to people with emotional
issues, such as anxiety.

The underlying basis of the traditional approaches is
their seeing the problem of anxiety as in the mind and
therefore the solutions lie with the mind. Additionally, a
therapist must be involved in order for the client to find
solutions. These two aspects are central to all traditional
approaches.

But, do these traditional approaches actually work?
Many years ago, in studies and meta-studies in the 1970s
and 1980s, it was demonstrated that probably 70% of the
clients improved on their own with or without any in-
tervening therapy whatsoever. There was no mention regarding curing or actually resolving any presenting issue.

In recent years, there have been some studies and books published indicating that not only is the type of treatment received **not a factor** of therapeutic success (however that may be defined), but neither is the theory behind any method nor adherence to particular techniques. However, the therapist's belief is a factor, as well as their personality. The relationship between the client and the therapist was also found to be a key factor, and beyond trust, likeability is critical. One can conclude that we do not exactly know why any therapeutic intervention works, but we do know that it requires another person, requires a very long time, and the relationships between the therapist and client is critically important. The definition of success is never consistent across therapists, even within any particular method of therapy.

All of these traditional approaches have these basic understandings and are key points to remember:

- The client's thinking is distorted and impaired (i.e., "stinking thinking").

- There has to be a relationship between the client and therapist in order to achieve therapeutic goals; this is critical

- A therapeutic goal is to work together to increase awareness of more healthy strategies for the client—strategies for easing or coping with anxiety.

• Therapy will follow a long course to reach a therapeutic goal, since the client has impaired thinking that needs correction.

• It is fundamental and necessary for the therapist to facilitate improvement of the client and provide insight for the client.

# Chapter 7
# **Newer Approaches**

Continuing our analogy of fighting with anxiety, we have moved out of the Dark Ages and now have better weapons. This chapter covers a few approaches that go beyond traditional therapy and attempt to involve a patient's body and their own energy in the healing process, including hypnosis; neurolinguistic programming; somatic body approaches like bioenergetic therapy; expressive therapies such as dance, art, drama, writing, and journaling; as well as meditation and mindfulness. These newer methods are moving us away from therapist-directed approaches and closer to Energy Psychology (Chapter 8) and even REIN (Chapter 9).

## Hypnosis

Hypnosis has its historical roots in concepts of the occult, magic, and stage show. It is new and different when used in a therapeutic setting. Hypnotherapy differs in that the therapist works while their client is neither conscious nor unconscious. Its application is mostly directed at altering a person's behavior. An individual with an emotional issue, such as anxiety, exhibits a set pattern of behavior indicative of that anxiety. Addictions (e.g., overeating, smoking) and other compulsive behaviors lend themselves to treatment with hypnosis. Hypnosis itself implies that a person is in a state of mind other than consciousness (nor subconscious)—in a state somewhere between. The client has perhaps more focused attention, yet they are relaxed. The basic principle of hypnosis is that, while in this in-between state of consciousness, the client has increased suggestibility. The hypnotherapist will supply the suggestions.

The brain wave pattern of a person in a hypnotic state is truly different than their normal wakeful or sleep patterns. The earliest form of hypnosis suggested that this was a state of increased mental alertness, but somehow leading to a more progressive relaxation. Commonly, hypnosis occurs when another person guides or leads another person by way of induction into an altered state. In this altered state, the hypnotized person is open for changes in their subjective experience like a behavior; this, in turn, changes their emotional state; and, finally, that unwanted the behavior is eliminated.

A therapist named Milton Erickson improved upon and amended hypnosis in developing his own type of hypnotherapy. He used indirect rather than direct suggestion. Since indirect suggestions are disguised, they are less likely to be rejected by the individual receiving them— that is, not readily rejected by the conscious mind. Erickson used this indirect suggestion method, engaging the unconscious mind to actively assist the therapeutic process. Erikson himself thought it was also of benefit for the therapist to go into a trance to help the client. He certainly believed that the unconscious mind was always listening, whether the client was in a trance or not, and the client would respond to suggestions as long as there was a mutual vibration or resonance at the unconscious level, between the hypnotherapist and the client.

Erikson believed the unconscious mind was definitely open to opportunities and to symbols and metaphors and especially to contradictions. He was purposefully vague with his hypnotic suggestions to allow the unconscious to fill in the gaps. A creative hypnotherapist can construct these gaps to suit the particular client in ways that are most likely to get the desired change.

As an example, the direct suggestion, *"you will stop being anxious,"* when dealing with someone who has anxiety is less likely to have an effect than the phrase, *"you can become less anxious."* The first is a direct command, and the second is an opening, an invitation, no pressure, and there is no resistance to that. Erikson introduced a variety of clever suggestions, penetrating linguistically into the subconscious, including:

*Would you like to go into trance now or later?*

*Would you like to go into trance while standing or sitting down?*

*Would you like to go into trance with your eyes open or your eyes closed?*

*Would you like to experience a light, medium, or deep trance state?*

*Would you prefer to get over your problem with a rapid but more intense method, or with a gentle method that takes a little longer?*

The last suggestion is incredibly clever: framing a meaning of success to the client's subconscious and even framing it as an option to happen slow or fast. Erickson understood the impact of confusion on a person. The subconscious mind of a confused person, since their conscious mind is occupied, is increasingly open to accepting reasonable suggestions. A confused person is in a trance all by themselves.

Guided hypnosis with a trained therapist approaches problems in a unique way: attempting to make use of the subconscious mind. Success in hypnosis more lies with modifying behavior than it does with modifying emotional states, such as anxiety, stress, or fear or all of those degrees or shades of fear along the continuum between fear and loving bliss. Nonetheless, in terms of modifying behavior, it certainly acts more rapidly than other forms of traditional talk therapy. Results are also measurable. If hypnosis is used to quit smoking, results are easily observed—or nail biting, or drinking, or other behaviors unacceptable to the client. Self-hypnosis is sometimes taught in conjunction with hypnotherapy homework, or by itself as an independent substitute for guided hypnosis. The principles described above remain the same.

## Neurolinguistic Programming

Using many aspects of Ericksonian hypnotherapy, there is another developed therapy approach called *neurolinguistic programming* (NLP), which was advanced by Richard Bandler and John Grinder in the 1970s. Employing the language of computer, one of the claims of NLP is that it helps people change by teaching them to reboot their brain's internal programming. This is the same conditioned programming refer to in earlier chapters. One could think of NLP as brain software modification. It relies heavily upon the idea that the unconscious mind is constantly influencing conscious thought, and thus behavior or action. It relies also on the fact that metaphorical (symbolic) speech and suggestion (like Erickson's) is critical in this reprogramming. Also, NLP relies on confusion so it is definitely in agreement with Erickson's concepts.

NLP has a particular set of tools to assist the client in getting what they want. If getting what we want is to remove them from an emotional state of anxiety, this appears to lend itself to that purpose—in theory, anyway. There are many of different and clever methods with which this can be done. NLP is an approach that looks to the positive more so than the negative. It is an approach *toward* as opposed to *away* from something; modeling is the foundational basis.

NLP relies on modeling where a client is taught to adopt another's behaviors, language, strategies, and even beliefs in order to construct their success model, emphasizing proven strategies. This modeling is about patterns and these behavioral patterns that are in the conscious mind. NLP relies extensively on Erickson's work as well as some of Virginia Satir's, and even Fritz Perls with his gestalt applications. NLP modeling is concerned obviously with modeling exceptional people, successful people and helping to achieve client's goals. When a client models correctly, they are actually suspending their own beliefs and taking on those of whom they are modeling. The very concept of modeling of course is not exclusive to an NLP approach, but NLP takes it to another dimension of observing. Simplistically (but realistically), if someone else can do something, you can also learn how to do it. You can model and follow that person's pattern of language, thinking, and beliefs. You end up reprogramming yourself according to that model. Then, you can achieve your desired goal—that is, what you want.

An inventive aspect of NLP is that the client gains awareness of their own patterns that were producing the undesirable outcomes. NLP also subscribes to the idea that each of us has a primary representational system, which is a tendency to think or learn in a particular way. We do so either visually (by seeing), aurally (via listening), or kinesthetically (manually doing). A client's learning style is then used in the modeling—the NLP practitioner also connects to that client's subconscious using their representational learning system to improve communication. An NLP practitioner, in knowing the client's primary representational system, can match that and easily "dance" with them; they can match the client's moves and, in doing so, enhance their communication.

Even though, NLP requires interaction between a therapist and a client, NLP can be learned for an individual's self-practice. Just like Ericksonian hypnotherapy, NLP provides an artistic way for each of us to gain access to our subconscious.

## Somatic (Body) Therapies

There are some interesting direct somatic, or body, approaches to consider when dealing with emotional issues, such as anxiety. The first type of body therapy is called *orgone therapy*, and a psychoanalyst named Wilhelm Reich, a protégée of Sigmund Freud's, developed it. Reich worked directly with individuals' bodies rather than looking at the content of what the individual was thinking or saying. Reich looked more at how the body actually exhibits—physically demonstrates—what the mind was thinking: how the face, the arms, the entire body moved and reacted. At the same time, he saw that there was this tremendous amount of muscle contraction within the body, which he called *muscular armoring*, and this is what holds emotional issues. He worked with deep massage and especially body positioning in order to bring about emotional release with his clients. Reich is thought of as the founder of the term psychosomatic (meaning, the mind and body) relationship. Reich also practiced his therapy in a different way than his contemporaries: rather than sitting behind the patient, he would sit next to them in order to make the patient feel stronger. He would actually touch the person in a manner so that he could truly be aware of their tension and its location. He attempted to obviously relieve tension, this armoring, with his massage of sorts. He would answer the client's question but in a different manner rather than the typical response of a therapist analyst at that time, which was, "Why do you ask?" He certainly delved into an area that in his time was taboo, and that was sex—and Reich did this in a completely different way than Freud. His concept of orgone therapy had to do with the ultimate mechanism of release of all body armor: that is the male and female orgasm.

Reich was one person in the Western world who also spoke to the concept of bioelectricity, which he observed in patients' bodies and called "the flow of energy." This was very new thinking for the Western world.

One of Reich's students, Alexander Lowen, expanded on his work and became one of the first researchers who dealt with the tension and the physical rigidity of movement in the body, which he believed was a direct expression of the total mind. In many ways, Lowen narrowed in on the exact definition of emotion: if we experience something related to a thought, we will have this experience in our muscles and in our subsequent movements. He was only thinking about the musculature and not the entirety of the body, which includes all the internal organs and systems. He developed bioenergetic therapy, and while it uses the conscious mind, it primarily works with the physical body. Although Lowen, by training, was a psychotherapist, the cognitive aspect of his work did not consist of exploring the individual's past as related to the current issue. But, rather, his methods, with use of the client's body, gave them a chance to become aware of their emotional issue directly. This means awareness within their bodies, where they were actually experiencing the issue.

When you work with a bioenergetic therapist, you work in an individual session, and you work with your body through specific physical postures that are designed for you. These postures elicit different vibrations in your body that are related to the amount of muscular tension. The therapist will also work with you hands-on and have you move your body in different positions. You do not have a single session; you have many sessions as you work through specific emotional "blocks" in very specific different parts of your body. The emphasis here is that, much like most therapy approaches, it requires another person to do it with you. It still makes use of the mind in talking and discussing the past, but it does work directly with the body so you have a concept of where this stuck emotion of anxiety might live within the body.

## Expressive Therapies

Expressive means to show or physically reveal, so expressive therapy implies doing something by you. There are also different expressive types of therapy, and these include such things as dance therapy or drama therapy, art therapy, and maybe writing or journaling as well. All of these therapies have one thing in common: the person can, with the use of their body, examine feelings simultaneously with their thought processes.

For example, art therapy (within a professional relationship and guidance), is where one is creating art, and the client can increase their awareness of their particular symptoms related to their emotional issues by expressing these issues on paper with different mediums. The purpose of this awareness is to maybe weaken the symptoms,

PART THREE **THE PROBLEM SOLUTIONS**

or at least find ways to cope with them. It is based on the belief that a creative process is a healing process that reduces emotional intensity and increases self-awareness. The same holds true for other expressive therapies.

Dance therapy is excellent because it is based on the idea that the body and the mind are one, and that the body and mind interact so that a change in movement, this movement of the dance, affects mind and it becomes therapeutic in a nonverbal manner. There are many particular dances that have been commonly taught using this therapy, but essentially the therapeutic process does involve a therapist who works with the client. The therapy would progress through a variety of stages, and in the end, you would have an investigation, discussions, and analysis with the therapist, to evaluate your particular emotional issue, like anxiety. The outright resolution of anxiety is not really addressed. There is supposed relief and easing of anxiety, or perhaps learning how to cope better with anxiety, since we are using the body. Maybe we would have to be continuously dancing or moving to maintain that relief?

Akin to this, there are many Eastern approaches that utilize the entire body such as Tai Chi, Qi Gong, martial arts, and yoga. There are many types of each of these as well; there are tens of variants of martial arts, several varieties of Qi Gong and very many branches of yoga. With many of these methods, you may or may not be guided, but in the end you alone are using your body. Whether these approaches, like dance, bring about transformational changes in dissolving the negative emotional state of anxiety, is at the heart of determining their efficacy in our evaluation.

Drama therapy is an expressive therapy where an individual intentionally uses a *theater process* to perhaps ease some particular emotional issue. They are acting out directly or indirectly their particular issue. This lets the client actively work through his experience in storytelling and acting out in the theater. This hypothetically eases or diminishes emotional issues like anxiety or at least permits one to cope better. This drama approach arises from the evidence that there are many issues in life that are too painful to look at unless you pretend. Pretend to be someone else, and act out in an imaginary story thereby expressing that "someone else." Given we see so much emotional instability of movie and TV actors, one might think this is not that effective. However, drama therapy works well with children since their programming is less entrenched and their imagination has been less smothered. Drama therapy is often used in conjunction with other types of psychotherapy, and it tends to also be coordinated with the cognitive mind (thinking) therapies.

Another type of expressive therapy is called writing therapy, where the client works under the care of a therapist or a counselor, and writes about their problem, such as anxiety. This process of writing is intended to be curative, in and of itself, as it theoretically releases or eases tension. In writing about one's feelings related to some particular trauma, this emotional state of fear is addressed by creativity, thus lessening the emotional reaction.

There is an adaptation that is probably even older

than writing therapy: journaling. Here, you keep a diary of everything that happens and record your meaningful thoughts and, most importantly, your feelings on a daily basis. This is of particular benefit since once you start putting down something on paper, you are using your body to do this, and the body is where the emotions reside. The difficult issues of the day that you are journaling perhaps become less etched with anxiety. You ease your issue as you use your body to write freely. This, in theory, calms the fears related to the swirling torment of thoughts continually looping through your anxious mind.

Visualization or Guided Imagery therapy is yet another type of therapy, but not exactly expressive since the body is not involved. The mind is used, but not the body. This therapy has been used to treat a variety of different mind and body issues. The concept is that when the visual cortex of the brain (where we actually see) is activated (without receiving any input from the eyes), it changes the physiology of the body through its relationship between the physical body and the emotional state. A good concept. It is a mind–body therapy, and it is thought of as something that is anti-stress, but it has its effect in reducing symptoms related to many medical issues as well. It has been around for thousands of years, from the healing temples of ancient Greece to people traveling to Mecca or to Lourdes, where people would try to visualize themselves to health. Even today, Christian scientists use visualization as a tool for inner change. Visualization was used by the ancient Essenes, by the Rosicrucians, and the Kabbalists. All had the common belief that there was a mind over body manifestation. What you "imagine" you're move toward. Again, emotions reside in the body, so if we use something that is indirectly controlling the body when trying to resolve emotional issues, we are then working with the emotions themselves. There are a variety of practitioners in modern day who have written many texts and CDs that expand upon this visualization process.

Affirmation (which means saying something positive to ourselves) is an expressive therapy and includes carefully constructed statements or phrases that are used as a tool for creation of positive outcomes. The concept is that in using affirmations on a constant and daily basis can negate years of negative self-talk. The power of these repeated positive statements is thought to override or erase all of the negative programming that has brought us to this emotional state of anxiety. Its benefit is that a person has the ability to do it by him or herself. The challenge is that the positive statement that you are repeating to yourself must have resonance and validity so that it gets input into your system. There are not necessarily bad affirmations, but there are ones that can border on nonsensical. For example, if one has anxiety about being short, saying "I am 6 feet, 2 inches tall. I am 6 feet, 2 inches tall. I am 6 feet, 2 inches tall," repeatedly ad nausea when you are 5 feet, 8 inches, is not going to achieve your growth to that height. Similarly, a 50-year-old man may repeat affirmations about his making a professional basketball team, which of course is nonsensical. If his affirmation was to write a best seller, that could be a possibility. So, affirmations need resonance together with some type of sensibility or credibility to be valid and feasible for positive outcomes.

Visualization and affirmation presuppose that the mind, the conscious mind, can control the body—the body where emotions reside. Our emotional state of being is a pattern that is embedded in our body. Visualization and affirmation techniques may momentarily override that subconscious programming, regarding a current emotion that is arising, but these cannot permanently alter an emotional state of being.

## Meditation

Meditation, as well as the Buddhist's concept of mindfulness, has come into vogue—beginning with transcendental meditation (TM). TM was popularized by Maharishi Mahesh Yogi and was very fashionable starting in the 1970s. Since the Beatles were advocates, it became trendy around the globe. Another Indian mystic, Krishnamurti, also developed his own style of meditation producing a similar large number of followers. There is also Buddhist-derived Tibetan meditation and Japanese Zen meditation—with sub-variants in each. There are many, many more different methods of meditation.

The intent of meditation is to have you enter into a no-mind state, from the periphery of your consciousness into your core being. The central idea is that while the conscious mind creates questions, it simultaneously creates problems. Solutions to our problems lie not in our mind, but in the no-mind and its connectedness to the universal mind or universal consciousness. Solutions are not found or generated in the conscious mind, nor the unconscious mind, but in the universal mind—or, as some would call it, the super-conscious mind. We can connect to this universal consciousness through meditation; solutions to an issue like anxiety would arise from here.

The mystical side of Islam is called Sufism and Sufi whirling is a fascinating, active meditation. It is not only beautiful to watch, but emotional states changes occur easily even for the inexperienced. Another highly educated mystic, Osho, started a movement and ashram in Poona, India, in the 1970s and eventually founded an additional ashram in Oregon in the 1980s. The media inaccurately labeled him as the "sex guru" and seemed incapable in their understanding of his meditation techniques. Most Osho meditations are active, and freely used concepts from several Sufi mystics. Osho meditations and their effect are astonishing even for a complete beginner.

The use of the body by itself tends to move us into a no-mind state. If we are totally in our body, then we cannot be in our conscious mind. Meditation, and there are many different types of meditation, tries to move us from the conscious mind, passing through the subconscious, and into the universal consciousness. Solutions exist here, not problems.

If we stop and think for a minute, we may realize that the mind basically functions by inquiry, by asking questions. Even now, your thinking may be, "Is this true?," which is itself a question. However, solutions are not in the mind. They come from the subconscious or its connection with a universal consciousness—our imagination.

Einstein said imagination is everything and his accomplishments, his solutions came to him not in long hours of computational or analytic thought, but from his non-conscious mind. He credits solutions materializing and coming to life while asleep.

## Conclusion

All therapies discussed in this chapter are different and some are newer in application as well as unique in their approach to dealing with emotional issues such as anxiety. They are not about using the mind to "figure out" solutions, nor endless dialogue. They are not about talking, talking, or more talking. These therapies tend to look at the intersection of the body and the mind in their application and not exclusively with the mind. Key points to remember include:

- Hypnosis uses a different state of awareness (between conscious and subconscious) in its attempt to handle the subconscious mind. The Erickonsian hypnotic method cleverly addresses the subconscious mind by using confused indirect suggestion. It is useful for modifying behavior.

- Neurolinguistic programming uses Ericksonian language. It employs a vast array of methods to help the client to achieve their stated goal. NLP astutely uses a variety of the mind's representational systems to affect a modeling approach to achieve a desired goal for the client.

• Reichian and Lowen's approaches work directly with the body in an attempt to resolve emotional issues.

• Expressive therapies are active and use the creative body process, in and of itself, to ease emotional issues.

• Meditation is in vogue now and there are many, many types; the most easily learned and immediately effective are active meditations. The end purpose is for the participant to enter a no-mind state.

A no-mind state allows solutions to arise.

This is neither an all-inclusive nor highly detailed list of approaches or methods, but this information should provide expanded understanding. Simply having a brief summary of some traditional and newer methods increases our scope of knowledge and strengthens our foundation. The stronger our foundation, the better our ability to grasp and then try radical or outrageous approaches that realistically can find an immediate solution to anxiety. It helps us to understand that we do not merely need to accept anxiety as a normal part of our existence. We do not have to live with or just cope with anxiety.

# Chapter 8
# **Radical Approaches**

The field of Energy Psychology is the newest tool used to counter anxiety. Based on the work in Applied Kinesiology, Energy Psychology focuses on your body's energy systems, specifically regarding storage, balance, and flow of energy to resolve stuck emotions, like anxiety.

## Energy Psychology

Energy Psychology (EP) could certainly be classified as a radical approach to solving emotional issues, especially as related to anxiety. But practically it should be simply considered a cutting edge approach. So, what exactly is EP? We can look to the Association for Comprehensive Energy Psychologies (ACEP) for clarification. This association is where like-minded therapists have come together since 1999 from a variety of different fields to receive education in EP, receive workshop training, get certified in EP, participate in advanced study, and perform or conduct studies as related to EP. There are about 3,000 members located around the world and they are healers from a variety of different fields. I would encourage the reader to go to the ACEP website and to take a look. The ACEP is an organization that was founded by some gifted, brilliant, and astute therapists with different areas of expertise and experience. They have set grand objectives and goals that are being met and exceeded. Under their purview, there have been 100+ studies and papers written (to date) demonstrating the efficacy and duration of EP methods.

The executive director, the officers, and the board members are extremely dedicated, informed, knowledgeable, and broad-minded individuals, open to new ideas, open to new understandings, open to new therapies, and open to new research—all with the goal of providing the best possible care for their members, patients, or clients. ACEP's definition of Energy Psychology is as follows:

> **"Energy Psychology (EP)** is a family of integrated approaches to psychotherapy, coaching and healthcare treatment rooted in mind-body healing traditions that are up to 5000 years old. EP methods blend the bio-energetic insights of those traditions with the best of contemporary psychological practice, and they have been refined through 35 years of clinical experience with millions of clients throughout the world. Energy Psychology gently and swiftly releases traumatic events that are frozen in time in the mind-body system. These events negatively influence how a person sees the world, experiences and regulates emotion and relates to other people. Embracing what modern physicists and ancient wisdom traditions know, Energy Psychology acknowledges the role of bio-energetic systems within and between

people as important determinants of health and well-being, illness and pathology. Energy Psychology theory suggests that psychological problems are a reflection of the disturbed bio-energetic patterns within the mind-body system. This system involves complex communication between a person's neurobiology and their cognitive behavioral emotion patterns. Energy Psychology practitioners combine cognitive interventions (including focused awareness and mindfulness, imaginable exposure to traumatic memories and cognitive reframing) simultaneously with the stimulation of one or more of the human bio-energy systems such as meridians, chakras and biofields. This powerful combination facilitates rapid positive change and optimal psychotherapeutic outcomes and is aligned with the latest findings from neuroscience and traumatology. With over 50 research studies to date, EP meets the criteria to be designated as evidence-based treatment."

This current definition has evolved and expanded over the last 16 years and currently is more like an explanation, perhaps in an effort to assuage traditional organizations in psychology and medicine. Let's go back in time a bit and elaborate, yet simplify, the concept of EP in this manner:

The **root cause** of all stuck and negative emotions is **disturbances** in the energy fields (the bio-energetic fields) of the body including the Aura, the Chakras where energy is stored, and the Meridians in which energy flows. Energy Psychology, with a variety of approaches, addresses the root cause by correcting the disturbed bio-energetic field(s) or energy flow within the body.

This definition or description of EP is certainly in alignment with the newest findings of neuroscience, and there are, to date, about 50 research studies that show both the efficacy and the safety of EP. The ACEP recognizes that there have been approximately 100,000 people who have been treated and received benefits from EP such as:

• Reducing anxiety and depression.

• Healing trauma, including posttraumatic stress.

• Healing addictions.

• Overcoming limiting beliefs about relationships and finances, etc.

• Enhancing performance in sports, school, business, and in the arts.

We should emphasize again that the fundamental premise of EP is that the cause of all stuck negative emotions is the disturbed energy field related to that person's body. This is in sharp contrast to traditional counseling and therapy that presumes the problem is within the person's mind (thinking)—that is, the problem exists in the mind and the solution is found by working exclusively with the mind.

Energy Psychology is fundamentally different from the traditional therapy process. It is an exciting and fascinating way to look at someone's issues in that, using any of the variety of EP processes, results can and remarkably do occur quickly; these results are both observable and measurable to both, the client and the therapist. The results last.

The purpose of this book is to present the REIN process so that an individual can importantly understand and use it to resolve their anxiety and extinguish their anxiety by themselves; therefore, it is critically important we have an understanding of how this comes about. In order to have an understanding of what's behind EP and the REIN process, and where it comes from—its roots—you must have a solid foundation for actually implementing and using it. It is not magic—it is cool, it is fascinating, it is exciting; it is rooted in psychology, physics, and the neurosciences; and it is something of tremendous benefit to anyone. Its efficacy and value can be seen and tested immediately.

## Applied Kinesiology

Energy Psychology is based on the clinical findings from the field of Applied Kinesiology (AK), which were discussed in a previous chapter .One of the fundamental premises of AK is that there is benefit to look at a "triad" of aspects for foundational health for the individual. On one side of the triangle is structure (bones, joints, connective tissues, and muscles), on the other side is chemical (the body's biochemistry including foods), and on the third and final side is mental or psychological (traditional viewed as being the emotional aspect). Proper health relies on a balance of these three parts. Another fundamental premise of AK is that there is a distinct relationship between the body's muscles and organs and with the meridians of Traditional Chinese Medicine. Meridians are where life's energy (*qi*) flows.

AK says that you can ask questions while letting the body provide the answers by muscle testing. The muscle testing is not to test the power of a given muscle but rather the entirety of the body's response to a particular question. Beyond this, there is another complementary underlying premise: the body never lies. You merely need to ask the right question—and assess the question's response with muscle testing. In essence you are by passing the conscious mind for truth.

In the mid-1970s, there were more than a thousand or so practicing Applied Kinesiologists who came from various fields, including chiropractors, dentists, MDs, DOs, and specialities of urology, neurology, psychiatry, and a significant number of clinical psychologists. Dr. Goodheart and his close colleagues noticed that there was an important emotional component to the patient's presenting problem. This is fundamental to AK, if that emotional component was present and then left uncorrected, it would limit the patient's (client's) ability to come to a harmonious, balanced healthy state.

He and his colleagues, through the methodology of trial and error, found that a particular acupuncture point on the small intestine (SI) Meridian, the third point (SI-3), was significant. When stimulated, SI-3 seemed to have the ability to clear any emotional issue related to physical problem for which they were being treating. Whether SI-3 was stimulated by digital pressure, needling, or even tapping, the response was consistent to bypass the body's conscious sensory input so he used tapping mostly. Prior to this, Dr. Goodheart used tapping the skull in another technique. After his years of research in Traditional Chinese Medicine (TCM), Dr. Goodheart uncovered this technique called *temporal tapping*, wherein one could go directly to the subconscious mind without filtering from the conscious mind (or its experience or its sensory inputs). The area for tapping was around and above the ears on the skull. Bypassing the sensory inputs one could put suggestions, verbally or with writing, into the subconscious mind. This may be where the idea of tapping began, rooted in TCM 3000 years prior!

An Australian psychiatrist, Dr. John Diamond, was fascinated with the concepts of AK testing and asking the subconscious questions to get at the interior of the mind and verifying these answers with muscle testing. Over many years and in discussions with Dr. Goodheart, he expanded and developed this field called *behavioral kinesiology*. This expanded on the relationship between muscles, organs and meridians and the emotion related to specific meridians. Muscle testing was the tool he learned and used from AK. Simplistically, Dr. Diamond used positive statements with select acupuncture points to treat emotional issues of patient's health with a focus on stress (anxiety). This was not necessarily about treating the emotional part of a person's health problem, as other AK doctors were doing, but treating a psychological issue by itself. This was new.

Dr. Roger Callahan, a psychologist who lived not far from Dr. Goodheart in Michigan, was also intrigued by the concepts and methods of Applied Kinesiology. He developed sort of a cookbook recipe approach using these techniques and began the process of tapping as a full-fledged form of psychological treatment. He tapped Meridian points that he himself with his research correlated with emotional problems while the patient *simultaneously focused* on their problem. He discovered that if a person focuses on a specific fear at the same moment they are tapped, the fear could be removed, perhaps permanently.

He had a *eureka* moment with a particular patient who presented with a chronic stomach problem; after tapping a point underneath her eye (a point the stomach meridian), her symptoms completely disappeared. Dr. Callahan, in his zeal for finding a precise methodology, eventually found (through trial and error) that there are different points for different emotional situations, and he called these particular sets of points *algorithms*. He called this concept *thought field therapy*. If a person is holding a thought intensely or that thought is overwhelming for that person, then there is a *field* associated with that thought. He had one algorithm for fear, another for anger, another for hate, another for grief, and so on. He developed an approach to cure phobias quickly and named it the "5-Minute Phobia Cure."

Gary Craig, a student of Dr. Callahan, took this a bit further and certainly was influenced by Dr. Diamond's finding that stimulation of certain meridians and specific acu-points brought about changes in emotional states as well as treating any stuck emotional issue associated with a physical condition. Craig diverged to develop a single algorithm approach rather than a variety of algorithms for each particular emotional issue. This algorithm was very inclusive of most or all of the Meridians, and tapping them at select points. He called this methodology the *emotional freedom technique* (EFT). There are thousands of EFT practitioners around the world today, and there are excellent training programs for licensed healthcare workers to learn and gain expertise in EFT.

## Methods

Today, Thought Field Therapy (TFT) and Emotional Freedom Technique (EFT) are probably the most widely used and the most influential therapies in Energy Psychology today, and from which a lot of different techniques have been derived.

Over the past 20 years, offshoots of these original approaches (EFT and TFT) have been developed, including BSFF (Be Set Free Fast), EDxTM (Energy Diagnostic and Treatment Methods), ESM (Emotional Self-Management), ETFT (Evolving Thought Field Therapy), FFFF (Freedom

From Fear Forever), HBLU (Healing the Body Level Up), HSE (Human Software Engineering), PEAT (Psycho-Energetic Aura Technology), Seemorg Matrix Work, TAT (Tapas Acupressure Technique), TEST (Thought Energy Synchronization Therapy), and three-in-one concepts. There is no lack of approaches, but they do all involve the Meridians—putting pressure on the Meridian point(s) in some sequenced manner therein affecting the emotional state.

Not surprisingly, there are numerous healing practitioners who have come into the field of Energy Psychology who do not use Meridian flow of energy at all, but rather look to the Chakras, where energy is stored as their treating method. There are also healers, who work with the Aura of an individual as their mechanism for treatment of emotional issues. Some practitioners possess the extraordinary "sense" to see the Aura. However, most use their "sense of feel." The ability to feel the Aura can be cultivated for most people.

## Universal and Open

Energy Psychology training is available to all licensed practitioners wanting to attain a basic understanding of what EP is and its protocols. After training, each practitioner can then apply a basic treatment methodology in order to solve their clients' emotional issues. The foundation of all EP, as previously discussed, is that the cause of all negative stuck emotions is a disruption in the body's normal energy systems: the Aura, the Chakras, and the Meridians.

PART THREE THE PROBLEM SOLUTIONS

The mind, dialogue, inquiry, directions, or communication are not cast aside but certainly used. These are just cleverly used as a tool, not as, the end-all. The conscious mind is not viewed as the place where solutions are derived—the solutions simply do not lie there. The fundamental premise is that a person emotionally stuck in a particular place—in anger, fear, anxiety, hate—is there because your normal energy fields or systems are disturbed; and, the disturbed field that is imprinting your body in a certain *patterned* way related to that associated emotion is now your "normal." It is not that your mind has a problem. It is not that your mind needs readjusting. You may or may not have "stinking thinking," but your energy systems are disrupted; these disturbed energy fields need correction to return you to a normal state.

## Measurable

In most, if not all, of EP therapies, it is important that we measure and test the individual's state prior to any treatment. It is not merely asking a client how they feel or giving them a simple stress or depression questionnaire. EP is different. This measuring or testing is an important, unique, and a critical aspect for practitioners to remember when using EP, regardless of any particular approach. This before and after testing also differentiates EP practitioners from other therapists' methods.

Testing can be done in two particular ways: (1) What does the client feel? This is subjective, of course. So, a subjective unit of distress (SUD) is elicited where the individual says specifically what level of anxiety (or anger or guilt or any other shade of fear) they are experiencing. They rate it using a scale from 0 to 10. There is also another, more objective way to test: (2) Muscle testing. The truth of their subjective unit of distress (SUD) or any question can be validated by muscle testing (given that the practitioner is trained and adept in performing muscle testing).

Testing before treatment is important. Testing after is obviously important as well because whatever EP methodology is used—whether it be with stimulating acupuncture Meridian points in a certain way following some method or protocol, or by altering the Chakras, or even by manipulating the Aura of an individual—there is a valued measurement at the end of a session. With testing and measuring, both the therapist and the client become instantly aware of what has been changed.

## Conclusion

Energy Psychology (EP) is going to continue to expand and grow, and procedures will be streamlined. It is a field that has not been necessarily dogmatic, save its research protocols. EP is an approach that is open to different practitioners using their own methodologies. Because it is not so encumbered by traditional approaches and open to new methods, it will expand rapidly, providing valued benefit for so many people.

There are many excellent books, regarding energy medicine and Energy Psychology and most can be found by contacting the ACEP at their website as a starting point.

PART THREE  THE PROBLEM SOLUTIONS

There is a great wealth of material in these EP books providing understandable and straightforward information, primarily because of the high quality of writing. There are also many books about EFT and TFT along with all the other alphabet soup of techniques that were born from under the Energy Psychology umbrella. Their commonality of approach is that they all want to work with the client's *"disrupted"* energy fields.

There are also, sadly, many unlicensed and unknowledgeable individuals—who may be great communicators, authors, or public speakers—who put forth "tapping" solutions for literally anything. I thoroughly understand their enthusiasm for something that works so effectively as the methods of EP. I am not disparaging their intentions; perhaps, they have even found one or more EP protocols that were beneficial for them, so they want to share it. You could probably find a video showing you how to "tap" to find a good plumber, or to improve your knitting, get rich, get smarter, get better grocery prices, or get rid of your gray hair! However . . .

## IT'S NOT ABOUT TAPPING—IT'S ABOUT FIXING DISRUPTED ENERGY FIELDS

So, a cautionary warning: it's not so much that you will be harmed by "willy-nilly" tapping, but rather you will not have any chance of having success for your real issue, especially if your desired goal is to avoid existing in an anxiety state of being. Knowledge matters. Your understanding and comprehension matter. Protocols matter greatly. Experience matters. If you are using some tapping scheme from a YouTube video or a magazine article to resolve an issue, disappointment will greet you. You will either get no result or one that appears okay but is assuredly fleeting. Even when using an actual practitioner, if they are not treating you with genuine, proven Energy Psychology techniques and protocols, you will end up not only with temporary outcomes but you will find yourself disillusioned since any positive effect will fade quickly. Then, sadly you will lose any enthusiasm about the incredible results available with Energy Psychology.

# Chapter 9
# A Totally Outrageous Approach

Perhaps it is outrageous to think that you might actually be capable, given some knowledge and tools, of resolving your own anxiety. Is it outrageous that you can do this without alcohol, marijuana, cocaine, Xanax, opioids, or spending months (or years) in therapy reliant on another person? It is my belief that it is not only possible that you can do this yourself, but it is highly probable. Let's examine an outrageous blended fusion of approaches called REIN as a really, really futuristic (but available now) weapon to attack your anxiety state of being—a weapon that could have been developed by Doc McCoy and Spock together in the Star Year 2930.

### Resolving Emotional Issues Now (REIN)

This chapter is where we put everything together and provide you with a step-by-step solution to anxiety. It is not about your finding better ways to accept or merely cope with your anxiety but, rather, it is about actually dissolving your anxiety. REIN is an approach that does away with your emotional state of anxiety; in the worst case, REIN will lessen or mitigate it, so that you spared from dysfunction. At this point, it is assumed that you, as reader of this book, would prefer to remove yourself from an anxiety state of being. Know that having anxiety is okay— since it is natural—but living in a constant anxiety state of being is not natural or healthy and it keeps you un-resourceful.

All emotions are sensible and usable and necessary— they are part of our fabric of who we are—and we feel the entire range of emotions any given day. Emotions are the driving forces that move us toward the directions that we want to go and away from that which we want to avoid or away from that which prevents us from going where we want to go. Anxiety is something that we experience daily throughout our lives, all of us, every day. Anxiety is actually a shade of fear, a degree of fear—as is stress. In Chapter 1, we discussed a line (or the double line), that continuum, that graphically represented our emotional range from fear to loving bliss. Our emotional being, where we predominantly reside, is somewhere along that continuum. If we find that anxiety is our state of emotional being, it would seem reasonable to get out of that state, sooner rather than later.

In the last 5 years of practicing Energy Psychology and constructing and developing and refining the REIN technique, I have had the incredible opportunity to have therapeutic contact with 2,400 people in various countries all over the world, ranging in age from 7 years old to 80 years old. In all 2,400 of those therapeutic sessions, I have yet to find one situation where REIN could not resolve the issue of anxiety, stress, or fear—or, in the worst case scenario, lessen it such that it became an insignificant part of that person's emotional being. In doing this, I acted as the role of the therapist with the client; however, I gave them abbreviated techniques for their own personal use. I continue to find myself in humbled awe at the power of Energy Psychology and in particular the REIN process, not only for actual resolution of emotional issues like anxiety, and the speed in which this happens, but for the duration of the results.

The purpose of this book is to expand the relevance of REIN to a larger audience. It is about teaching that you can solve the problem of anxiety for yourself quickly with incredible efficiency. This chapter is devoted to detailing the REIN process, step by step by step. I begin by outlining the seven steps, giving you the big picture. Then I provide the specifics of each step followed by the details of each step. Each step is described with sufficient explanation so you have a thorough understanding of what each step means and why it is necessary.

## Relevant and Applicable Background

The REIN process was born out of a variety of techniques that I have mastered. The first of those is Applied Kinesiology, and as an Applied Kinesiologist, I have treated about 16,000 patients over 25 years of practice, performing perhaps in the neighborhood of 500,000 muscle tests and evaluations regarding almost everything imaginable including emotional issues; essentially, tests that unveiled fear as the obstinate issue preventing resolution of a particular physical problem. Besides learning from Applied

Kinesiology, I practiced acupuncture (both Chinese and medical) for a similar number of years, acquiring considerable insight about how Tradition Chinese Medicine (TCM) approaches and treats emotional issues like anxiety, stress, and fear. I became proficient at moving energy (qi) between acupuncture Meridians (the TCM channels of flow of energy) and moving energy (qi) from one direction to another, sedating channels or tonifying them.

Besides the inter-communication skills gained from treating 16,000 patients, I also acquired extensive counseling experience working as a jail chaplain and counselor for 5 years, and 8 years as a counselor at a homeless shelter, and additionally training counselors for 2 years for their work with women complying with the federal mandate in ending their reliance on public assistance. This wide-ranging experience, knowledge, and skill set attained in communication, counseling, and in-the-moment transactional analyses has been extremely productive. It was training beyond compare. Apart from Applied Kinesiology, acupuncture, and these many years of counseling, I trained in Ericksonian hypnosis and neurolinguistic programing (NLP). Certain techniques from NLP have been incorporated into the REIN process. Lastly, as a meditator for 30 years, I have adapted some useful measures from several types of mediation to be used in REIN as well.

REIN is therefore a combination and masterful blend from many healing disciplines. Each of these disciplines, individually by themselves, has been used in the attempt to solve the problem of anxiety. The reason to fuse and blend is that, possibly, the sum will be greater than the individual parts. Hopefully, $1 + 1 + 1 + 1 + 1 = 7$. Let's take the best from each method, mix them together skillfully, and you can possibly find an innovative, effective, and enduring process to resolve the issue of the anxiety state of being.

Learning the REIN process is not complicated, but it is something that one will have to learn and attentively **do**. It is not magic, it is not weird, it is not voodoo, nor is it akin to taking something temporarily to numb you to anxiety or zone you out. Neither is it absurdly mystical like putting a penny on your fourth toe, spinning around three times, and whispering a mantra to make anxiety disappear. It does not happen that way. REIN is a process that, if understood and followed methodically, will be of immediate value and benefit to you.

It is perfectly okay if you want to stay in an anxious state. If your emotional being is one of anxiety and you're ok with that, that is fine. When and if the time arises that you want to move from emotional state of anxiety, upward to the right along our continuum of emotional state of being (Illustration 2), then REIN will provide a path to do that—a fun path from which you can immediately gain benefit.

## Shades of Fear

Anxiety is a word, the same as *stress* is a word, but both of them are really type and degrees of fear. They are gradients of fear. They are shades of fear. They are nuances of fear. Anxiety is a word we say to ourselves. We are hesitant and we do not necessarily freely use it with colleagues, with friends, or with relatives. This is because of our perceived awkwardness or even embarrassment of being vulnerable, but anxiety can be expressed using different terms. We do this.

We could also say, *I am really panicked. I am feeling terribly insecure. I am so confused. I am concerned. I am scattered. I am helpless. I am nervous. I am afraid. I am worried, worried, worried.* However, even then we also don't readily utter these phrases aloud to others. Stress is also a degree of fear—a shade of fear—and using the term stress is socially acceptable. We can easily express to others that we are *stressed out*. We may want to back off that somewhat at times, and say we are feeling a bit burdened, or uptight, or we are overloaded, overwhelmed, really tense, and even burned out. However, we generally admit to being stressed out. Nonetheless, being in a state of anxiety or using our more socially accepted term stressed means being in a state of fear—as graphically seen along our emotional line or continuum. It is unhealthy to be stuck in an anxiety state of being as it keeps us un-resourceful and dysfunctional. As stated before, if you are stuck in anxiety, you are just a reactive reflex to the whims and events of life. When you want to get "unstuck" and move in the direction toward loving bliss, then the REIN process will do that for you.

## The REIN Process

Outlined here are the seven steps of REIN.

**1**

**BE AND UNDERSTAND YOUR ANXIETY ISSUE or DETERMINE IT**

… then rate it ,rate the strength of this issue on a scale of 0 to 10, with 0 being no issue and 10 being an extremely strong issue.

**2**

**FIND A SPECIFIC ANXIETY-PROVOKING EVENT CURRENTLY OR IN THE PAST**

Rate the strength of this event-issue on a scale of 0 to 10, with 0 being no issue and 10 being an extremely strong issue.

**3**

**NLP EVENT MANIPULATION PROCEDURE**

**4**

**YOUR BODY'S ENERGY SYSTEMS PREPARATION**

**5**

**YOUR SPECIFIC ANXIETY ISSUE STATEMENTS**

PART THREE **THE PROBLEM SOLUTIONS**

**6**

| PERFORM THE ENERGY TRANSFORMATION SEQUENCE |
| --- |

**7**

| CHAKRA SPIN AND ANCHORING |
| --- |

This diagram represents the flow of the steps and outlines how this process unfolds. Please note, to ensure success, all of the steps need to be followed exactly as they are presented. Missing or skipping steps will stop REIN from being effective for you. Let's examine each individual step and explain how and why it works.

### 1. Understand Your Anxiety Issue, or Determine It

Anxiety is a degree or shade of fear. What is your anxiety (fear) that seems to be with you all the time—that anxiety that is the undercurrent in your life? Your concept of fear, or what word(s) you select to express your anxiety, is important. One person might express fear as *tenseness*, another as being *uptight*, and yet another as *panicked,* or one might simply say *anxious.* The word or representation is your choice; it is important right now that you select words that are relevant to you, to your particular way of speaking, to your vocabulary, or way of understanding. It is absolutely not necessary that you use the word *anxiety* in your description. Unless, of course, if that is the word you would use when you sense your fear. It is important to use a term that you find resonates with you. Please understand "resonates." It means it has to be something that vibrates through you. It is not about analyzing a term but a word or phrase that expresses what you are *feeling*. It could be tense, worried, frantic, stressed, hectic, panicked, anxious, afraid, jittery, or so many others, but it is something used by you, for you, and whatever resonates with you.

So you can certainly say, "I find myself always worried," or "I always seem to be worried." You could use *stressed, panicked, annoyed*, or any term that you choose but, while selecting, use the phrase below and fill in the blank:

"**I find myself always** _____**,**" or "**I always seem to be**_____**.**"

You are going to have to determine this for yourself—ponder—but not deep analytical thinking. Simply see what bubbles up. Ask yourself about this, and quietly wait to see what comes up. For example, if indeed you have sense that *panic* best resonates anxiety for you, then use the word *panic*, in the statement to yourself: "*I find myself always panicked*," or "*I always seem to be panicked*." Or it could be something like irritated. Then you would say, "*I always seem to be irritated*." If you are indecisive, always then you would say, "*I always find myself indecisive*," or, "*I always seem to be indecisive*." Obviously, if you are already **in** an intense state of anxiety there is not much thinking that is needed, only that you simply express what is currently resonating with you.

If you are having difficulty expressing this, even to yourself, it might be advantageous and even informative for you to ask a loved one, friend, relative, mother, father, spouse, or partner to fill in that blank for you: "You always seems to be _____." It might give you some insight as to what degree of fear is evident and radiating out to other people.

Once you select your term, it is necessary to rate this particular anxiety (fear); we call this rating a subjective unit of distress (SUD), and it is something that you need to do without very much thinking. Do not analyze, do not evaluate, just let the SUD bubble up from the subconscious quickly. Understand that zero means there is no anxiety (or panic, as in our example) and that a rating of 10 means that it is absolutely disabling you. You are the only one to decide how much of an issue this is for you; you are going to decide this and place a rating value on it. Rate it from 1 to 10.

I want to point out that if you find that you are ranking an anxiety issue between 0 and 6, either one of two things is happening. One, you are not being really honest with yourself or, two, what you are addressing is not a critical issue for you. Not being a critical issue means you're not stuck, uncomfortable maybe, but it's not keeping you in an un-resourceful place. However, you can certainly still work with this anxiety issue, even just to get familiar with the REIN process. It is your choice. If there is a real anxiety issue, your subconscious SUD rating is going to be a 7, 8, 9, or possibly 10. However, simply be kind to yourself, think about the anxiety issue you want to address, and give it a rating. Don't make it more complicated than needed. At the end of this first step you should have a clear declarative statement and write it down, such as, *I am always panicked and it is at a level 8.*

## 2. FIND A SPECIFIC ANXIETY-PROVOKING EVENT

Examine and look within to find, or discover, a specific event that has created, or is currently creating, the anxiety for you. It is *mandatory* that an event that has triggered a high (but not disabling—see next paragraph) level of anxiety be brought to the center of your attention. There may be one, or ten, or a hundred events. You can select one that has intensity, and one that has an SUD rating of more than 6, but perhaps less than 10. You are the only person who knows this. If you want, you can choose an event less than 6 just to practice the entire REIN process—see how well it works for you. It is your choice, but good sense might dictate you crawl before you walk and you walk before you run. So take something small as your test project. We all have thousands of compelling events that have happened or are about to happen that create a significant amount of anxiety (fear) in our lives. Select an event that has a strong feeling of anxiety or relates to the representative word you chose—which, in this example, is panic.

Please take note here: If the event is so strong that it is something you do not want to think about, like an intense past trauma, then it is probably not appropriate for you to use that event. Find another one. There is really no need to address the worst event that you have ever experienced. We do want something that has a strong rating such as 7,

8, 9, or even a 10 but only if it does not evoke an excessive reaction for you. If there is only an intense event, then it would be best to work with a licensed therapist in this instance. Take another situational anxiety issue and word associated with it. For example, it may be panic (fear) related to speaking in public. Use this. You are the one who is going to determine this. You are the one who is going to find this event, and bring this event into your focus.

Then, take a piece of paper and write down: "This event is _____," and write a just a few lines about it so that it goes from your mind to a piece of paper. You will write the rating of that event on this paper as well. Now you are going to think about that event, bring your attention to it. In doing this, you will consider what it looked like, what it sounded like, what you were saying, what you heard, and where you were feeling anxiety in your body.

## 3. NLP EVENT MANIPULATION PROCEDURE

We are going to apply a simple NLP method to reduce the event's anxiety load, making it more manageable. We have been and are continuing to reflect on this event. Next, I would like you to look at a blank wall out in front of you and think of it as a large movie screen. You will imagine that the event is occurring on this screen, as a movie exactly as it occurred in the past. Pretend on this motion picture screen that you are seeing yourself in a movie regarding that event. In other words, you are not just watching the event, you are actually in this movie. You are part of this movie. You have the leading role. You are watching you.

Begin to experience and feel the anxiety that is coming

up. Make note—on the same piece of paper on which you wrote about the event—of where you feel the anxiety in your body. Do you feel it in your throat? Do you feel it in your gut? Do you feel it in your eyes, face, legs? Where? You need to be sure that you are actually associating yourself with this event visually. Your eyes are open. You are looking at this movie screen, and watching yourself in a leading role. This is not a still picture but a movie. You are also noting all different things about this movie: color, sound, action, anything of your choice. You are also the director. Explore what you are watching with all of your senses. The qualification here, as before, is that the event should not be an intense trauma issue that overwhelms you. The idea here is to be associating with a profound anxiety-producing event, not a crippling one. *That is not necessary.* The reasoning will be addressed in Chapter 10.

Now, you are going to take this movie, the movie of your event, making sure you are center stage feeling the anxiety issue, and then take the big screen in front of you, as big as it is, and make it a little bit smaller—perhaps half the size. Keep the movie running and be sure you can still see yourself in it, still feeling your level of anxiety. Make it a little bit smaller, half that big again, and then make it even a little bit smaller, half again, and then move that movie screen down to the right-hand side of the wall in front of you and make it as small as your cell phone screen. I want you to squint and keep looking right at that movie screen. See yourself in that tiny little movie screen. Now let the screen go black, and stop watching immediately and clap your hands three times as loudly as you can. This step is complete.

## 4. YOUR BODY'S ENERGY SYSTEMS PREPARATION

Here you need to have your body's energy systems reset to neutral, so to speak, without any basic underlying disturbance. Remember, any process in Energy Psychology is one that works with the energy fields of the body—the Aura, the Chakras, or the Meridians.

In order to get your body's energy systems prepared and ready for this process, we are going to make sure that there aren't any neurologic disturbances beforehand creating a faulty energy pattern. We are making sure that, energetically and neurologically, up is up, down is down, right is right, left is left, in is in, out is out. There are many excellent ways of getting the energy systems ready. However, the method included in the REIN process has proven useful and all-encompassing in most cases.

The REIN process (and most EP approaches) requires effort and activity on your part—it is not being done to you, you are the doing. You need to actively go for this to be effective. This is not going to happen with you lying down on a couch.

Next, stand, raise your left knee up in the air, and slap your right hand to your left knee, releasing that, and then raise your right knee and slap your left hand to that right knee. Then, alternate with the opposite leg and arm, and continue doing this, switching back and forth, while making sure you are fully breathing, not holding your breath or taking little sips of air. Breathe, keep alternating, and keep doing this. *No rush, just relax and enjoy.* Start very slowly, maintaining your breathing and then continue alternating, even start humming a song—any song you like.

You can sing it if you want to, and continue to breathe. Humming or singing ensures that you're breathing well. No one is watching you or listening to you. Go for it. Then, speed this up: singing or breathing deeply for 30 seconds while still alternating sides. You need to be active and putting out a full-hearted effort. This cannot be emphasized enough because if we do not have your body's energy systems prepared to be altered, then any change that you effect upon these energy systems is not going to be successful or last very long. If you are physically unable to stand while doing this, you may sit down. No problem at all. The emphasis is on getting the arms to the opposite knee and alternating and breathing and humming (or singing) as described; and you should increase your pace as much as you can, according to any limitations of movement. Adjust as needed. This will feel very good to you. After the 30 seconds, you are going to stop. The body's energy systems are prepared, and ready. The next thing we are going to do is called "generating a statement."

## 5. YOUR SPECIFIC ANXIETY ISSUE STATEMENTS

In step 1 you took much effort to look at exactly which anxiety issue you wanted to address. You also selected a word that represented your anxiety issue. *Panic* was used as an example, but it could have been any word that resonated with you, with or with your anxiety state of being. It could have been *scared, anxious, apprehensive, afraid, worried,* or *stressed* or a myriad of other words—the caveat being that you had to choose a word that resonated within you. You will be using this word now being mindful of the initial rating and how it felt in your selected event.

Place a large mirror in front of you, or stand in front of a large mirror. You can do this sitting down or standing up. Look into this mirror and into your eyes and, at the same time, notice that your eyes are looking back at you. This is something we rarely, if ever, do. We always look at our hair, our nose, or lips, teeth, or other features, but not into our eyes. This is a very simple but vitally important step. So, look into your eyes, look into your heart, without doing or saying anything for 30 seconds. This is an important step for you to do as we continue. For 30 seconds, you are going to look into this mirror. You do not have to think anything at all, just look in to see who you are. Relax and enjoy while looking into your eyes. You are looking into yourself, and your self is looking back at you.

As you continue to look at this mirror, after 30 seconds you are going to recite a very, very specific statement you've prepared. You will be saying it **three times**, but one portion of the statement will be said differently each time.

To demonstrate, we are going to continue to use the example of *"panic,"* with the associated rating of intensity. Recapping, we picked an event related to our feeling of *panic*, we made a movie of ourselves in that particular event and time when we felt quite *panicked*, and we played that movie on a large screen on the blank wall, and then we shrank that movie down to postage stamp size. We followed this with step 4 by properly preparing our body's energy systems so that a disturbed energy system could truly be adjusted.

Now that we have looked into the mirror (and the mir-

PART THREE **THE PROBLEM SOLUTIONS**

ror has looked into us) for 30 seconds, continue to look into the mirror and *slowly, **with great emphasis,*** say the following statements:

(1) "**Even though** I have (**a lot**) of <u>panic,</u> it is okay. I accept that. I accept myself exactly as I am. I love myself."

Followed by,

(2) "**Even though** I have **(some)** <u>panic,</u> it is okay, I accept that. I accept myself exactly as I am. I love myself."

And finished with,

(3) "**Even though** I have **(a little)** <u>panic,</u> it is okay, I accept that. I accept myself exactly as I am. I love myself."

Say these phrases with a lot of attention, intention, vocalization, and expression on your face. You are not only looking into the mirror to see your eyes, but you are also watching the fact that you are going to be expressing with great conviction, that you are going to be moving all of the muscles of your face, even your eyebrows, and you are going to be moving your jaw. You are going to be putting a lot of expressive intent into these statements.

There is additional critical and pivotal element to add, which should be done while you are repeating these statements. You are going to be simultaneously stimulating points on the sides of both of your hands against each other—rubbing, tapping, or making contact with these points. These are acupuncture Meridian points: specifically, the small intestine 3 (SI-3) as shown in Illustration 8. SI-3 is a point on the small intestine Meridian that is the master point that governs another point of the governing vessel (GV-14). GV-14 is the control point for all of the yang channels of the body. And, yang is creator of excess energy; so yang can create over-excitement. Yang is hot; anxiety is hot. Yang can establish anxiety. You will be sedating yang.

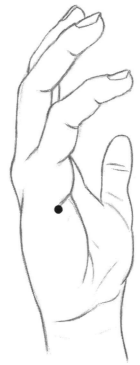

Illustration 8: Small intestine 3 (SI-3) Meridian point.

Why are we stimulating a particular point on the body? Energy Psychology and REIN attempt to correct a disturbed energy system of the body. In this instance, the Meridian system is altered with stimulation, and this continuous stimulation is sedating. The flow of energy is altered. Again, a held thought in the mind—a held thought like the event that we were just picturing on our movie screen—that particular thought changes our body's energy fields. This in turn instantaneously changes the physiology of your body. The result is an emotion. The emotion that we are talking about here is anxiety or, in our case, we were talking about feeling *panic*. We want to correct the disturbed or disrupted energy systems—the Aura, and/or the Chakras, and/or the flow of energy in the Meridians—at the exact same time as we are neurologically processing this event together with our resonating word. This was on its way to becoming a *panic* emotion taking residence in our body. We are interrupting that.

So, look into the mirror for 30 seconds, look into your eyes, and then recite the three statements with **"a lot"** the first time, **"some"** the second time, and **"a little"** the third time while simultaneously stimulating the small intestine point (SI-3) on the side of your hand. These SI-3points can be stimulated by rubbing them, by pinching them, by tapping them, or even approximating them and moving each of the hands in close proximity together. Striking the hand together exactly at those SI-3 points is sometimes called *karate chopping*. You can do it any way you choose to as long as you stimulate both SI-3 points. It is important that you do both, so why not simplify and do both together. This step and all the steps before need not be rushed—no need to be speaking quickly or stimulating points rapidly. Take your time and be methodical in each aspect of the step. Keep in mind that you are speaking loudly, actively, energetically, with intention, while at the same time looking into your mirror and stimulating SI-3. You, by yourself, are beginning to change your anxiety state of being. Relax, enjoy and sense your empowerment.

**Speed is not required but
methodical discipline is essential**

### 6. PERFORM THE ENERGY TRANSFORMATION SEQUENCE

This step is the very core of the REIN process. It is direct, straightforward, easy, and fun. Simply, you are going to speak a word while stimulating six specific acupuncture points while at the same time still looking into your eyes in a mirror. As you do this, you will be saying the word that is representative of your anxiety issue. So, in this instance, you use *being panicked* (a degree or shade of fear) and simply say *"panicked,"* as you stimulate each of these points consecutively. These points are shown in Illustrations 9 to 14, showing their exact body location.

These points can be stimulated by rubbing, pinching, tapping, using your fingernail(s), or even by just moving one or two fingers above and in close proximity to the point. It is your choice. You can energize them in any way that you choose. So you begin:

PART THREE **THE PROBLEM SOLUTIONS**

1. You are going to stimulate gallbladder 1 (GB-1). This point is on the outside of the eye as shown in Illustration 9. Although only one point is shown, there is a corresponding point on the opposite side. Do both together.

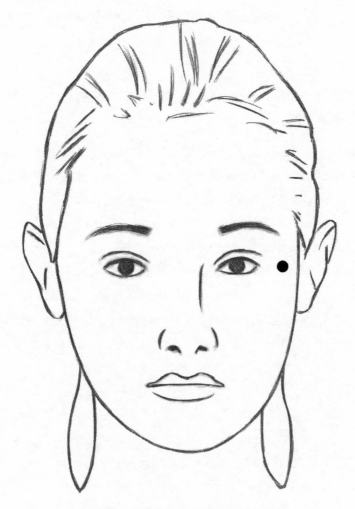

Illustration 9: Gallbladder 1 (GB-1) Meridian point.

2. The next point to stimulate is spleen 21 (SP-21). It is on the side of your body directly below your axilla, or your armpit, as shown in Illustration 10. Like the first point, do both at the same time, and you can use all your fingers to assure you get that point. This is the end point of the spleen meridian.

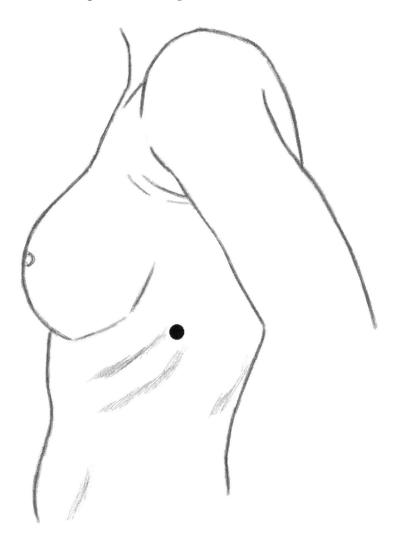

**Illustration 10: Spleen 21 (SP-21) Meridian point.**

3. The next point is liver 14 (LR-14), about four finger widths directly below your nipple; when you stimulate this particular point, you can do so with two or three fingers, so as not to miss the point. This is shown in Illustration 11. Both points are shown here. Do both. For a female, the breast tissue may need to be lifted. So, you can do one side after the other. This is the end point of the liver meridian.

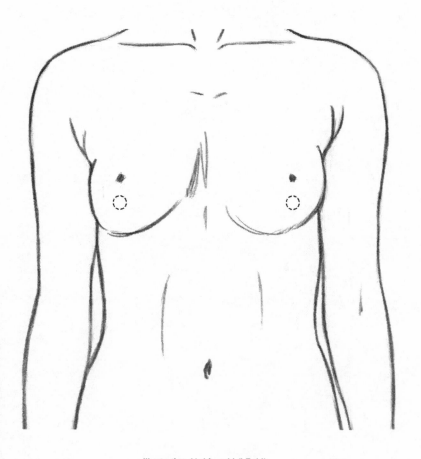

Illustration 11: Liver 14 (LR-14).

4. The next point that you are going to stimulate is small intestine 3 (SI-3), on the sides of your hands as we did in the previous step. This stimulation was shown in Illustration 8, but is repeated in Illustration 12. Do both at the same time.

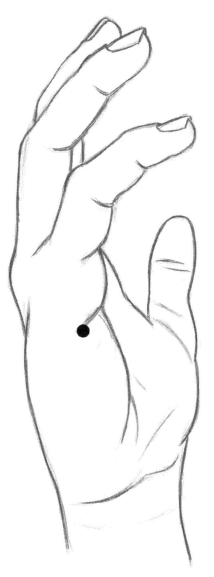

Illustration 12: Small intestine 2 (SI-3) Meridian point.

5. After that, you are going to stimulate point lung 9 (LU-9), which is on the wrist and is shown in Illustration 13. You can do each side individually or both together in a similar manner as you did for SI-3. This is the source point of lung channel and has much greater influence on emotional issues than the end point (LU-11).

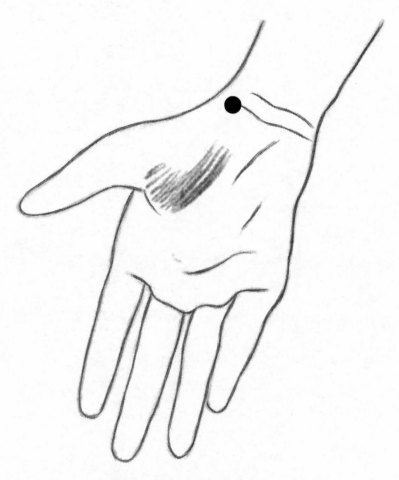

**Illustration 13: Lung 9 (LU-9) Meridian point.**

6. The last point to be stimulated is kidney 26 (K-I6). It is where your collarbone comes into your breastbone at the very top—it is those bumpy protrusions there. Use multiple fingers there as well so that you actually do not miss the point. This is presented in Illustration 14.

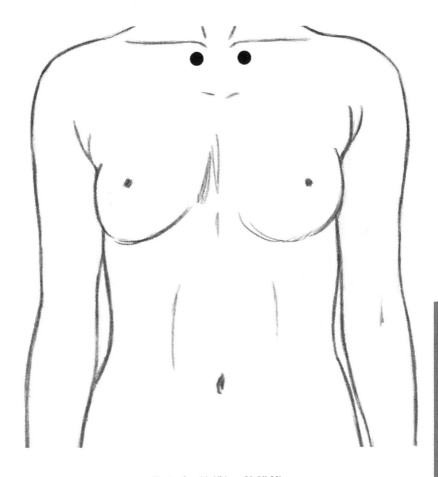

Illustration 14: Kidney 26 (KI-26).

Stimulate these points however you choose to, on both sides. Remember at the same time, you will be simply speaking the anxiety issue representative word, the emotion that is at issue here. In our example, we are using *"panic."* Since you will be doing this bilaterally, it may seem a bit tricky for LU-9; however, you can merely hold or rub your wrists together since you cannot do it on both hands at the same time. It is OK if you want to simulate one side first and then the other. With the rest of the points on gallbladder, the spleen, liver, kidney, and small intestine, you can easily do those at the same time. Perform the entire sequence **twice.** Repeating,

## Speed is not required, but methodical discipline is essential.

This is not about doing something for the sake of just doing something while we speak and this is certainly not a nonsensical method, like putting a penny on your big toe, spinning around three times, and repeating some mantra, therein hoping something is going to change. This is a definitive process that, once practiced, once done a few times, will become second nature—it becomes easy to do. There is no need to complicate this; it is all about your being in charge, and being empowered to readily dissolve your anxiety state of being.

## 7. CHAKRA SPINNING AND ANCHORING

The last step in the process is related to the Chakras. Remember there are seven Chakras as shown before in Illustration 6 and now seen in Illustration 15 (with some additional emotional information).

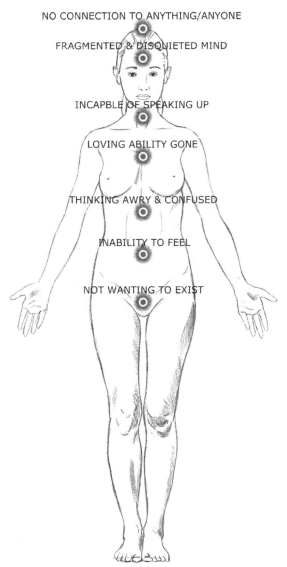

Illustration 15: Chakras and associated emotions.

Chakras are these places where energy is stored. Now, you are going to perform a technique called *Chakra spinning* that could be used to bring the Chakras back into balance, either by toning down an over-excited Chakra or energizing a weak Chakra. Here we are energizing weakened Chakras.

You will be starting at the bottom Chakra. At your groin is the root Chakra. Up from that are the sacral (spleen), the stomach, the heart, the throat, the pineal (or the brow), and lastly the crown Chakras. These are seen in Illustration 15. This illustration shows the Chakras and the resulting experienced emotions associated with each weakened Chakra. You will need to determine which Chakra is most applicable to your specific anxiety issue.

Looking to the root Chaka first, and if your anxiety issue (panic) is related to your **simply existing**, then select this Chakra.

Going upward and self-evaluating, you could further sense if your *being panicked* was truly related to your ability **to feel anything at all**. If you are *panicked* about being emotionally numb, then select the sacral Chakra.

Moving along, if your anxiety issue has to do with your capability of **thinking clearly** ("I'm in a panic because I just can't think straight ever") or controlling your thinking ("I'm feeling panic because my mind and thinking runs amok all the time"), then choose stomach Chakra. If your *panic* anxiety is about the fear/insecurity of your **ability to love** (to give or to receive love), or even about inability to trust, then the heart Chakra should be your selection.

If your *being panicked* is about your **inability to speak**

**up** for yourself and/or to communicate your needs and your desires, then the throat Chakra should be chosen.

If your anxiety issue regarding *being panicked* relates to **not having a quiet mind**, and that your mind seems to be running constantly and never gives you a moment's rest, then the pineal (brow) Chakra would be the one to select.

Lastly, if being panicked was about really being confused about the whole picture of life, and your **loss of spiritual connection** or **your loss of connection** with **other people**, then the crown Chakra is what you should select.

If you sense that your being *panicked* is not clearly specific to what we have just addressed, then it is up to you to see what it is most closely related to. Take your time. Here you can realistically use your conscious mind to do what it does best: ask questions. Ask and wait for the answer, the answer comes from the subconscious. If you find that feeling panic is related to more than one Chakra, then it's fine to work with more than one. Relax and do it.

### Spinning Technique

At this time, stand up, still while looking at yourself in that mirror initially, and put your **right hand** over the Chakra area that you selected. Use the mirror to find the right location for your hand placement. You will be closing your eyes as you do the procedure. Your thumb is going to be pointed straight up in the air, with the fingers pointed to the left. You are **not going to touch your body**; you are going to be just a half inch or an inch away, so that you are close but not touching your body, or your skin, or your clothing.

On Illustration 15, along with emotional issues and their correlating Chakras, there are also associated musical syllables (do-re-mi-fa-so-la-ti). Select the particular musical syllable that is related to your chosen Chakra as the most related to your *panic* anxiety issue.

For example, if you determined that your *feeling panic* had to do with your ability to love (to be loving, to give or trust), place your hand over the heart Chakra area and make the sound of the syllable "fa." It is best to give yourself an idea of what that syllable sounds like. You have to find which key you want to start in. Start with the root Chakra and say "do," then move up the musical scale so that you get the right tone.

You are going to move your hand **slowly** around *to the left* and then down in a small circular motion over that Chakra, again *not* touching yourself, while humming the associated musical syllable. Do this slowly and while relaxed, now keeping your eyes closed. Remember our mantra:

### Speed is not necessary but methodical discipline is essential

You are going to continue to do this for about 2 minutes. You are just going to relax into doing this. You are going to feel wonderful doing this. It is going to be very easy for you to do.

At the end of about a 1 minute —it does not have to be exact, just approximately—you are then going to gently and slowly let your right hand come to rest directly upon that Chakra. At the same time then move your left hand to the spot on your body where you had actually felt the *panic.* You will be anchoring that Chakra energy to another point that previously was your felt-area of emotional upset. You will create new point, an anchor, to access that Chakra and its energy directly at your affected body area.

Hold this for 30 seconds. You will actually want to hold it longer, and if so, enjoy and do it. As soon as you finish, open your eyes, take a big breath in, and exhale loud and long. Then think about the anxiety issue that you had and think about it in the context of the event that you had chosen. **Immediately** rate it, on the scale of 1 to 10, the anxiety that you are now sensing. Just quickly picture yourself there, in the previous event, within a matter of a half second. Then, write down how strong that feeling of anxiety, or in our case *panic,* is now. Don't think, don't evaluate, don't analyze. Let your subconscious present a number and write it down.

## Now What?

You are going to be feeling very refreshed and relaxed at this point in time. You will feel amazed when you see how that rating has dropped from its high down to 2 or 1 or even 0. You will be at a loss for words, which is irrelevant since words are of no value here. It is about how you feel and the sense of freedom you have gained. It is about your sense of empowerment in that you have done this by yourself. I also have to tell you that there is going to be a lot of *bewilderment* at the same time. The conscious mind is going to be confused because it does not understand what has happened. Without the conscious mind's control or consent, without its overriding authority, your energy field has changed; it has moved from a disturbed state, related to that held thought regarding an anxiety provoking event issue (*panic*), to a normal or balanced state.

The mind had nothing to do with it, so the mind is going to be very confused. Even irritated. The conscious mind is going to be racing all over the place, so be ready for confusion, and also be ready to be amazed, because I promise that after you place your hand on your Chakra, take that big breath, and sense the vanishing of the anxiety issue, you are going to be absolutely astonished.

I have been blessed to witness 2,000 or 3,000 clients experience this transformation of being amazed, astonished, and bewildered and confused—all at the same time.

When you think about that event where you felt *panic*, the thought about that event is still there. It has not been erased from your memory. It is there. However, there is no new analysis about it; there is no new strategy. The event exists and your thought of being *panicked* is still there, but the emotion *pattern* imprinted in your body is not there from the disturbed energy fields. All settings are new. There is no charge. You have transformed the disturbed energy fields.

The intensity of that *panic* that resided in your body is no longer there. Why? It is not there because the energy disturbance associated with it, the one that initiated an imprint in/on your body after the thought, is no longer there. Restoration to a neutral undisturbed or balanced energy field has taken place.

## Reflections

I fully realize that after reading the parts within these seven steps, you may be dazed a bit, because it is not simplistic. REIN is simple but not simplistic. There are a lot of words and explanation to try to give you a precise guide for this process. All of this detailed information is required and needed to compensate for not having an actual hands-on experience. However, performing the process without all the background before discourages the use of REIN irrespective of its effectiveness. In short, the more you know, the more you will effectively use it. Before laying out the REIN process, step by step, all the prior chapters hopefully presented you with sufficient foundational background and explanation to clearly give you a sense of purpose and why REIN can be successful.

When you begin to use this process, pick a small anxiety provoking issue for practice. Choose an anxiety issue that is important but not one that is not an overwhelming issue. It certainly can and should be an anxiety issue that you truly want resolved, no matter how small.

When using the REIN process it is important that, just like when baking a cake, the recipe must be followed EXACTLY. That cake recipe requires specific ingredients, in specific order, and things done in a prescribed way and in the end it goes in the oven at a specific temperature. This is similar to the REIN process. If you decide to omit one or two things in the recipe because you don't have them, you won't get a cake. If you want to omit some part of the REIN because it seems confusing to you, you don't like it, or it is bothersome, then you are not going to get the result—the dissolution of that anxiety. All steps must be followed, but there is no rush to do this. You are changing something. You are changing a disturbed energy system within you that may have existed for months or even years. No rush. The first time you do the process, you may be slow, even taking one- half hour or more. But as you gain proficiency, it will just take 10 minutes to go through all the steps. You may not be able to do it quickly as in any learning process, yet you are still going to get excellent results. Namely, the body's disrupted energy field is going to be changed; therein, the emotion-anxiety issue that resides in your body is not going to be there, and it is not coming back. It is not returning in a week, it is not returning in a month, it is not returning in 5 years. It has gone. It has changed. You have changed the body's energy fields. In changing the disrupted energy fields, and normalizing them, you have changed your body's imprinted pattern associated with that anxiety issue, and you have forever transformed the anxiety related to a particular thought or associated event. You have become unstuck, and you did it by yourself, without a therapist!

Besides following each of the seven steps in their sequence correctly and SLOWLY, there are some key points that you must focus on and try to perfect—not *be* perfect, but try to do them thoroughly. You do not have to do them quickly, just be methodical and thorough.

✓ **You must be event-specific.** It is not going to work very well if you attempt to treat the general issue of anxiety—or, in our case, panic—by just saying "panic" and not relating it to any specific event. The concept of it being specific to an event is critically important for the success of REIN.

✓ You must put energy into the preparation of your energy system. When you are going up and down with your hands to your knees and you are breathing hard, the faster you do it, the more effort you put into it (even if seated), the more prepared your entire energy system will be for the upcoming change.

✓ You must take time and effort to put strength into the statements that you are speaking—the statements that begin with **"Even though. . . "** All parts of these statements must be spoken clearly. The louder that you say them, the more you affirm, the more passion, the more body and facial motion you put into them, the better it will work. It is not sufficient to be docile and just read these statements like you are reading a book.

✓ As you do the energy sequence of step 6, it is sufficient here to just repeat the word without any great intensity. It is sufficient to stimulate each point for 10 seconds. You can relax as you are doing this, but be sure to stimulate both sides.

✓The Chakra spinning is a process that needs to be done in a soft and relaxed manner. There is no intensity that needs to be put into it—the same as we have discussed before. It is soft, it is easy. It is just a slow movement with the musical tone related to that Chakra.

This REIN process is an incredibly valuable tool that you can use to resolve your issue of anxiety. Remember, anxiety is fear, so we are talking about resolving fear. Fear has innumerable gradations or shades. In the English language, we have so many words representing these shades of fear that we use daily. The REIN process is powerful. You can think of it as a weapon of mass destruction, destroying your fear, anxiety, stress, tension, anger, sadness, etc. so that it is not part of your normal state of emotional being anymore.

**Key Points to Remember:**

- Continuously held thoughts disrupt energy fields of the body, if extremely intense or repetitive.

- Disrupted energy systems modify the body in its entirety.

- This body imprint change is, by definition, what defines emotion.

- All emotions are okay and occur every minute of every day of our lives.

- The perpetually disturbed body's energy fields

create the stuck emotion. This is one that becomes your emotional being; this keeps you in an un-resourceful state.

- The cause of all stuck emotional issues is a disruption of your body's normal energy systems.

- You can fix it by changing the body's energy systems.

- You can normalize the body's disrupted energy system, and you can bring it back to equilibrium.

- With rebalanced energy systems, you will return to a resourceful state.

## Conclusion

REIN is a process that is a blend of many healing modalities, both physical and psychological, both traditional and new. It was born from formal education and training, from acquired expertise, from intuition, and many years of experience. REIN has been tested, refined, and retested several times over almost five years, in an attempt to achieve both optimum effectiveness and ease of use. Each selected Meridian point in the **Energy Transformation Sequence** has been vetted with Applied Kinesiology techniques and muscle testing, in three different pilot studies and thousands of therapeutic client sessions.

In Chapter 8, Energy Psychology was described, and many different treatment methods were mentioned. Most involve tapping on Meridian points. Most tapping methods are therapist performed, although some do involve homework tapping by a client. Many practitioners and even nonprofessionals have fashioned their tapping sequences or formulas for almost anything. Looking on YouTube or online book stores, we can see tapping for money, real estate guidance, or a romantic partner, not to mention the ones for specific pain issues (headache, back ache, leg cramps, etc.) and tapping for many situations or emotional issues. Regardless of their training or knowledge (or lack thereof), my assumption is many professionals and nonprofessionals are presenting their "tapping" models with wholesome intentions. Good intentions or not, the challenge is that many of these simplified "tappings" may provide a quick good feeling but that it will probably readily disappear the following day. This leaves a person with less than positive feelings about Energy Psychology techniques. Energy Psychology is not about temporary warmth, but finding solutions.

When you are interacting with another person with whom you have confidence, and you are seeking guidance—there is trust and you want see some resultant effect. When you are working or tapping with a therapist or counselor of some other type, again with whom you trust, you are hoping for a solution, an effective solution to the presenting issue. The relevant question is whether you achieve a lasting effect, a solution. This should be your guide. It is not about finding a way for coping with anxiety. It is not about a way for ignoring anxiety. And it is not about accepting anxiety as part of life. It is about resolving your anxiety.

Anxiety can be blunted with pharmaceuticals, and symptoms of anxiety can be subdued. There is a multi-billion industry dedicated to just that. If the symptoms of anxiety are toned down a bit to enable a person to find solutions, then the temporary use of medication is applicable. Psychotropic drugs are not curative. Have you ever seen anyone achieve an actual solution for their anxiety with a drug? Perhaps there is one such person. Anxiety can be (and is) eased with alcohol along with recreational drugs on a daily basis everywhere on this planet. Have you seen anyone truly resolve anxiety this way? Perhaps there is one. Anxiety can be modulated with compulsive obsessive behavior. Have you seen someone become anxiety-free this way? Perhaps there is one. Exercise definitely curbs anxiety—is there anyone that has exercised his or her way to be anxiety-free? They would be very fit, but be thoroughly wiped out from exercising all their waking hours. As we all know smoking and food alter anxiety and almost everyone uses this option without thinking about it, or the consequences. Can you use smoking or pizza to become anxiety-free?

In the United States, there are hundreds of thousands of therapists of different types practicing cognitive (thinking) therapy addressing anxiety. Have you met that one person who has gone from an anxiety state of being to finding a solution to being permanently free from anxiety? Perhaps?

**Talk is not enough, drugs are not enough, activity is not enough, and destructive habits are not enough.**

PART THREE **THE PROBLEM SOLUTIONS**

Most arbitrary acupuncture point tapping formulas are not enough either. But, therapeutic intervention with qualified Energy Psychologists, of many different persuasions, has had excellent results over the last 20 years with **actual solutions** for anxiety. Clients have found both quick and enduring solutions—not just modifying or lessening anxiety or finding new clever coping strategies.

Sadly, not everyone has the opportunity or funds to participate in an Energy Psychology approach with an Energy Psychologist. The REIN process wants to give anyone existing in a state of anxiety an avenue to essentially resolve that anxiety—or, at a minimum, limit anxiety to a state of irrelevance for normal resourceful functioning. This chapter provided step-by-step instructions to do just that. This book itself is the result of having taught the REIN process in workshops around the globe for the last 4 years.

Is REIN for everyone? If a person's anxiety or other fears or stress reach the intensity where they may hurt themselves or others, then immediate medical or psychiatric intervention is required.

# Chapter 10
# **Anxiety Dissolved**

## You Did It! Now What?

Before looking at what might be ahead for you, let's recap and summarize all that has been explained, explored, and experienced.

In looking at any potential solution to a problem, it is both sensible and necessary to clearly and precisely define the problem. The problem is anxiety, and we understood that anxiety was best described as a degree or a shade of fear—and we are either moving in the direction of fear or in the direction of love, as we go through our day.

Anxiety, the emotion of anxiety, is merely a word that we use to express a degree of fear to ourselves and others. We, similarly, could have spoken of this degree of fear as stress or even tension. We could use representative words like worry, dread, jitters, scared, tenseness, and so forth to describe our degree of fear. We use the terms anxiety and stress since both are the commonly socially acceptable words that express our emotional degree of fear.

Anxiety was represented graphically (see Illustration 3), as one point on our emotional line—the line representing the emotional continuum between fear on one end and loving bliss on the other end. Expanding on this idea of an emotional line or continuum further, we took into account a possible intense event or repetitive events of significance by showing a split in the line as well as the changing slope of the lines. The intense trauma or the repetitive less intense events are the ones that create an increasing slope and that gap that stops us from easily moving toward our natural state of loving bliss. In Illustration 4, a few typical emotions were shown. However, if we had many, many feet of a line, every known emotional representative word could have been placed on this continuum—of course relative to our own language and our own culture.

We know that an **emotion** is a physiological response by the entire body to a held thought in one's mind. Even a fleeting thought can generate a physiological response. However, there is a difference between an emotion (all of which are 100% natural) and our emotional state of being. An emotional state of being is the place to which we end up residing in—that is, where we emotionally exist throughout the day or week or even years. Anxiety and an anxiety state of being are two very different things. Every day a person undoubtedly has a countless number of other emotions besides anxiety, minute by minute. Our range of emotions even within an hour or two may be numerous. During the day, you are continually going between moving in the direction of fearing or in the direction of loving. But we eventually settle back down to a particular "well" on that line; this is our home point, our emotional state of being. It could be that this place is being annoyed, irritated, scared, anxious, stressed, sad, or angry . . . so many little "wells," each of which describe a degree of fearing. It is not a state of the mind or personality—it is a state of emotional being, our inherent state. This is not to say that our resting point could not be at ease, contented, or happy.

In looking at the construction and/or components of the problem, we addressed the mind—the conscious mind, the unconscious mind, and aspects of each. In the simplest of terms, anxiety (and every degree of fear) is rooted in the body, which was the second part of the problem's structure—the body. Our bodies are incredible, operating pretty much on their own and doing great things for us constantly, but when we attempt to alter how it automatically operates, extreme and dysfunctional situations develop.

Looking at the last of the problem's components (the body's energy systems), Chapter 5 presented and detailed concepts of the three energy systems of the body (which was perhaps something new to you):

- The **Aura**, the total field of the body.

- The **Chakras**, where energy is stored, and can be visualized as whirling vortices of energy.

- The channels or the **Meridians**, where energy flows.

Anxiety is an issue for most of us, and we all want to at least reduce it, if not dissolve it completely. Anxiety keeps us in an un-resourceful state and immobile or stuck. There are assortments of common approaches in tackling anxiety, including thinking it through, drinking it out, or drugging it out. Initially, we may merely talk this through and discuss our issues with friends, relatives, clergy, or colleagues to lighten this anxiety (fear). We further considered cursorily some traditional "talk" methods that each used a professional as a necessary guide or partner for us

PART THREE **THE PROBLEM SOLUTIONS**

in their particular method. Then, some new and different approaches were outlined—such as, hypnosis and some body therapies. An understandable representation of the cutting edge approach of Energy Psychology (EP) was laid out. EP was only viewed as radical because of its fundamental premise: **the cause of all stuck negative emotions** *(in our case, anxiety)* **is a disturbance in the energy fields of the body**. Stuck negative emotions (*anxieties*) are not in the mind and are not of the mind. A continuing, persistent disruption in the energy fields of the body is creative of the stuck negative emotion—in our case, that is anxiety.

Since the cause of being in a continuing anxiety state is the disturbed or disrupted fields, it follows that the most useful and direct solution is found by focusing our attention to these energy fields, altering or transforming them through some process, and returning them to a "normal" non-disrupted condition. Our discussion included several Energy Psychology approaches, for which relevant treatment was about "fixing" the disrupted energy fields to resolve this anxiety state of being.

In Chapter 9, the totally outrageous REIN approach was presented—which was actually not as outrageous as it was **sensible**. It was sensible because REIN is a blending of the best of several different therapeutic approaches and assembling them into one concise method. This is how REIN evolved resulting in a seven-step, self-administered method that rapidly finds solutions. Each of the seven steps was clearly explained to give a greater understanding of how it all fits together. It would have been so much simpler (and faster) to just list the seven steps and say, "do this," but explaining and providing background information provides a rock solid foundation that creates confidence and the motivation to apply REIN.

All the other approaches commented upon relied on thinking it out by ourselves, talking to friends, or family, using professional talk therapy, using body work, or with trying expressive therapies to solve our anxiety state of being. They certainly have some degree of success in lessening and providing some coping ability. But, then again, so does ingesting lots of sugar, or chocolate, or caffeine, or cocaine, or crystal meth—as does sedating ourselves with alcohol, marijuana, Quaaludes, Xanax, benzodiazepines, or opioids. These all move us away from an emotional state of anxiety for a brief moment, however, we are subsequently and harshly snapped back to where we began, or perhaps even lower down that sloped line of our emotional state of being.

The majority of the traditional approaches to resolving emotional issues use the mind because of the common misconception that emotions are of the mind, even though therapists employing traditional methods know the fundamental definition of emotion. The idea that emotions are in the mind is erroneous and completely the furthest thing from the truth, by definition. Other approaches that independently look at the body for resolution are a bit more applicable since the body is the residence, the home of emotions. However, it does appear that these direct bodywork processes create more of an awareness of a dysfunctional emotional state than they do in dissolving them.

PART THREE **THE PROBLEM SOLUTIONS**

**It seems most of us live our lives not only unaware
of our resting state of emotional being, but also
unaware that loving bliss is our natural state, and
that there is a possibility and capability of obtaining
at least an equilibrium. We certainly remain unaware
that we could achieve our natural emotional state.**

Energy Psychology puts forth the radical or cutting edge concept that a held thought can and does disturb our energy fields—which becomes the cause of a stuck negative emotion, like anxiety. Energy psychology and its many, many approaches do find actual solutions that are rapid, verifiable, and lasting. The REIN approach is presented in Chapter 9 and is a straightforward, step-by-step method that only requires our attention to detail. It does not have to be done quickly. REIN can and needs to be done it at our own pace, methodically arriving at our desired end result—that our anxiety is dissolved.

## Where Does that Leave You?

In my treating 2,400 patients, and teaching this process to several hundred more, one thing is abundantly clear: **it works**. After REIN, when anxiety (stress, irritability, sadness, anger, panic, or whatever the degree of fear) is diminished to a level of 0 or 1, people experience incredible amazement, relief, and euphoria. However, this is followed closely by confusion or a mental fog created by the conscious mind. The conscious mind, and its driver the ego, wants to control things. The conscious mind has been mostly left out of the REIN process. We have cleverly used the conscious mind in rapport, dialogue, and instructions in NLP portions but it was unaware of the purpose for which it was enlisted. Although the mind was used, **the solution was not of the mind or by the mind**. So, now the conscious mind is racing around, creating confusion, creating delusion, creating denial, but the conscious mind will find this a challenge since a new reality is now in place! Amusingly, the conscious mind will then generate self-talk expressing that the anxiety issue was never a big problem anyway. When recalling the event that had previously created anxiety, we will remember it perfectly, but it will no longer holds charge, there will be no longer be a disturbed field, nor the ensuing imprint in your body (the emotion). In other words, there is no *experiential* anxiety. Essentially, the proof is in the pudding, and the conscious mind is panicked.

If you experience disorientation or strange self-talk after REIN, it is natural. Being surprised is common and natural. Five years ago, I was working with a basic EP process as part of a group for demonstration purposes and I used this basic process for my own anxiety regarding decision making, which I resolved in about 3 minutes. Even though I had used similar methods for my patients to eliminate the emotional aspect of their physical problems, thousands of times before, this was my first attempt to focus only on an emotional issue. I was amazed, thrilled, happy, and bewildered simultaneously. My own self-talk afterward was that decision making was not really a significant issue for me. I was assuredly confused, and my mind raced around denying the possibility—but in 3 minutes it was gone, wow! Five years later, the problem's resolution holds. The process remains effective! Yes, my conscious mind may say there is a challenge making decisions, **but staying resourceful I simply just make decisions,** not beating myself up whether or not they are made in seconds or hours. There is no disturbed, disrupted energy field when a decision needs to be made—thus, **no anxiety**.

What about you now after your anxiety issue is eliminated or radically reduced? If we look at Illustration 16, there certainly is a variety of possibilities. The first thing is that you are no longer going to be residing in one particular point on this slope. You are going to be residing someplace to the right and definitely not to the left. Your emotional being is perhaps not going to be stalled, or "stuck," in one particular place. Additionally, the angle of the slope could have possibly changed as well, making it easier to move to the right; that it is not so "uphill" for you. The gap between the first slope and the second slope may be narrowed. Depending on the intensity of the anxiety issue you cleared, you might even find a new resting place on the second slope.

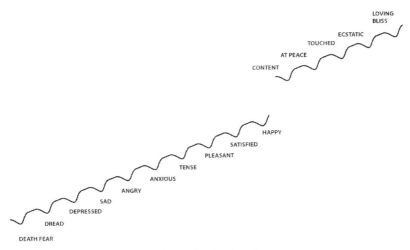

Illustration 16: Emotional continuum.

Once anxiety is cleared you are now left in a **resourceful state,** shedding your spontaneous reactive **un-resourcefulness,** where you were just being a reactive reflex to life. Life happens regardless of what we do, what we think, how we act, and how we feel. Life advances with continuing interactions and interpersonal relationships (at home, work, or play) are always fluctuating. Things are constantly going to be in a state of flux, in a state of change. This is how it is. What is going to change, once you are not fixed in the emotional state of anxiety, is that you are going to have the ability **to respond in any way that you choose**. That is, being **resourceful** and responsive. In contrast, when you were in the **un-resourceful** emotional state of anxiety ("panic")—or *stressed*, or *fearing*—then your response to the events of life were merely reactive reflexes. If a reflex, there is but one response, a disrupted energy field–induced body pattern (anxiety, stress, fear)

PART THREE THE PROBLEM SOLUTIONS

that reacts only in one way to ANYTHING unlikeable that occurs for you. It is like the physician taking a little hammer and tapping you on the knee, and your leg kicks out—you do not have a choice, you are automatically responding. A reactive-reflex is all that can happen.

If you are in an anxiety state of being, and life brings you a new situation, a new person (be it a friend, neighbor, potential mate, whoever), your reactive reflex is anxiety, panic, or stress—all shades of fear. When life brings a new child into your life, or a new work opportunity, there again fear, anxiety or panic will surface. When asked to give your opinion to a group, the same response. When things change from really good to really bad, which happens every day as that's what life is, there will still be that reactive reflex of anxiety. You can "think" all you want, even before something potentially happens, but the disrupted energy fields are still there and thus the emotional state of anxiety, which resides in your body, with its inherent imprinted pattern is always there. You are but a reactive reflex—a reactive reflex to life. If you use REIN to abolish the disrupted energy fields associated with your anxiety state of being, you will find yourself resourceful. When events happen in your life, if you are **resourceful,** you have the ability to calmly act in a responsible way, or as I like to say, to be *response-able.* You are no longer a reflex. You now have the natural ability to respond to a situation with humor, with surprise, with amusement, with curiosity—so many different ways—but you are not going to be stuck in this state of anxiety, stress, and fear, and just be reactive.

PART THREE **THE PROBLEM SOLUTIONS**

162

Being in a **resourceful** state means a state of calmness, lightness, playfulness, or even focused stillness, and it means a state of increased confidence because you have the ability to be *response-able*. You, now **resourceful**, have increased awareness, increased knowledge of the big picture of what is happening around you, and an awareness that life is always moving forward—with inherent up and down cycles, with good and bad, or that which is perceived good and perceived bad.

You, as a **resourceful** person, can relax into your own creativity and are freed up from *contraction*. All anxiety, all stress, all fear—remember all these emotions that reside in the body—reside in the body through neuromuscular **contraction** and use vast amounts of energy for no reason whatsoever other than to hold you fixed in space. **Fear equals contraction.** As anxiety is resolved, vast amounts of energy become available, improving everything that happens in your life, especially relationships with your family, with your friends, with your children, with your colleagues.

Our natural state of being, our inherent resting point, is love and bliss. Regardless of good intentions, life and the conditioning of culture and mother, father, teacher, preacher have moved our emotional state of being far to the left toward fear rather than to the right, toward loving. If you use this REIN process, deliberately, methodically, you are going to find yourself effortlessly moving toward your natural state.

PART THREE **THE PROBLEM SOLUTIONS**

## Limitations?

### *Why Was Only One Event Selected?*

At some point in time it will dawn on you, if it has not already, that you only were asked to select a single event associated with your anxiety (panic). You used that and your anxiety diminished to a level 1 or 0, or vanished to insignificance. However, the anxiety was related to that event that you chose—perhaps it was a work pressure issue such as panic when you get deadlines from supervisors. You selected this because of its significance to you. Although important unto itself, perhaps it was only a very event-specific problem. But what about when you have a first date; what about when you have multiple things to deal with at home with children, spouse, family; or what about decisions regarding finances; and so on, and so on?

By resolving your work-related panic, you may not have moved yourself completely from that anxiety state of being. This is not a real problem at all. First, you experienced empowerment that you, by yourself, can alter your energy fields using REIN, thereby overcoming a disabling emotional issue. Second, you have now the practiced the REIN steps. Third, you are now able to use REIN on another pertinent *panic* situation.

Tackling other events that provoke anxiety is part of the fundamental methodology of most Energy Psychology processes. You can think of your anxiety state of being (panic) as the top of a table with many legs—maybe one very thick leg, a few medium thick ones, and some thin ones. These legs represent your conditioned life events that induced panic. These legs are supporting your un-resourceful emotional state of being panicked. By resolving one panicked event, a leg is removed. If it was the very thick leg, then the table—your emotional state of anxiety being—would collapse and be gone! If the event represented a medium thick leg, or a small one, then you will need to use REIN several times—whacking away a leg at a time until the table collapses. But also take note that you may not ever need to attempt to work on the thickest leg at all, the one that represented your most intense conditioned event! Wow! Why? Because, if you remove a critical number of small or medium legs, the table collapses anyway. If that event, that thick leg, was the one that represented an extremely intense event, the one event you never want to bring to the forefront, then now with REIN, it becomes unnecessary to tackle that directly. This may be of profound significance to you.

### Physical or Sexual Trauma

Sadly, physical or sexual trauma is certainly present in most societies and around the world. Don't work on problems related to this type of trauma by yourself; most of the time, it is very complex, involving perhaps many emotional issues and many aspects of each of those emotional issues. Get the assistance and guidance of an experienced professional—this is where they shine. These severe trauma issues are best left to the licensed professional, the certified Energy Psychologist, who has had both direct training in this area and significant experience as well. They will be able to work with you, probably using the "table leg" analogy approach or some modification thereof.

### What Went Wrong?

When using REIN the occasion may arise that there is only a little reduction in the subjective unit of discomfort (SUD), say from an 8 down to a 5. What to do? First, be happy with yourself that you got a reduction! Then, relax and repeat the entire process from the very beginning. It would be unusual for someone to be proficient the first time through. REIN, through each step, is simple enough in theory, but it is easy to be less than methodical in application (as I know from experience). Looking into a mirror (and directly into your eyes) and simultaneously finding the point to stimulate and then saying the word is not second nature to you—**yet**. It will be with a little practice. If you repeat the process again and there is still no *change* in the rating number, we can move on to an additional step.

There is an interesting component to resolving emotional issues that Energy Psychologists call **Psychological Reversals (PRs).** This term and concept are taken from Dr. Goodheart and Applied Kinesiology (AK). In AK this is linked to a reversal in polarity. We do have a definite polarity (plus and minus) from top to bottom, front to back, and in to out. If there is a reversal then contradictory responses and incongruences may arise. You can think of it as a "yes" but meaning "no" and vice versa. An AK therapist can test this by a positive technique called "localizing" to KI-26 bilaterally, and switching can be corrected, although perhaps only temporarily. For me, as a physician and Applied Kinesiologist, in about 160,000 patient visits for general health issues, I saw PRs only about 10% of the time. However, in using Energy Psychology, it essentially means there is *incongruence* between what your conscious mind states as a response and what the nonconscious (subconscious) mind knows. As an Energy Psychologist, working with about 2,800 clients, that PR rate rises to 60% of the time—and to almost 100% in African boys and girls in reform schools or orphanages.

Energy Psychology deals with PRs beautifully and addresses the conditioned incongruences that are in conflict. These PRs can also be appropriately thought of as *hidden objections* to your success. You want to be calm, but the conditioned program says calm equals laziness; you want to have less anxiety, but the conditioned programming says having some anxiety is not only natural but needed for "success"; you want to express your sexuality, but programmed conditioning says good girls don't. There is a significant amount of excellent Energy Psychology literature about this and how to deal with the issue. Some EP techniques even address this **prior** to even doing their own process.

It is impossible to overestimate the importance of our conditioning, which is as profound and prevalent as green in Ireland . . . to a smaller or larger degree. These hidden objections are like gates that need to be opened as you walk toward your desired goal of resolving anxiety.

PART THREE  THE PROBLEM SOLUTIONS

These gates need to be opened lest you remain blocked—
or these are like barriers that need to be hurdled. These
hidden objections to your success are definite bottlenecks;
however, they can be addressed directly and efficiently
most of the time. But, things can get complicated quickly,
as there may be aspects of hidden objections within issues
and issues within aspects of the hidden objections—it can
get a little crazy keeping track of the layers. This is when
it becomes advisable to seek an Energy Psychologist who
has a grasp and experience with this challenge.

However, these hidden objections, psychological
reversals, are centered on the following concerns:

1. We don't *really want to* dissolve the emotional
issue (anxiety) at all

2. We don't want to have anxiety *100% resolved*

3. We don't believe it is *possible* to do resolve
anxiety

4. We don't believe it is *safe for us* to dissolve
anxiety (completely or partially)

5. We don't believe it is *safe for others* for
resolution (completely or partially)

6. We believe we will lose all or part of *our
identity* if our anxiety is dissolved

There may be other hidden objections but this list will suffice for now. We should be aware that it is highly likely that more than one hidden objection exists simultaneously; each needs to, and can be handled individually.

Here is a quick, streamlined procedure for possible resolution of psychological reversals. You can certainly attempt this but a therapist's assistance or guidance may be needed.

1) Remember and focus a little on that **event** associated with your anxiety issue (*panic*, in our example).

2) Start stimulating SI-3 (and continually to do so throughout this).

3) Look into your eyes in the mirror. An absolute must!

4) Choose from the statements below and select the one appropriate to your specific hidden objection and say:

    a) Even though *I do not want* to have _____resolved, *I do want* to have it resolved. I am OK with that, I accept that, and I accept myself; I love myself.

    b) Even though *I do not completely want* to have _____ resolved completely, *I do want* to have it resolved at ___%. I am OK with that, I accept that, and I accept myself; I love myself.

c) Even though *I do not think it is possible* to have_____ resolved, *I do think it is possible,* I am OK with that, I accept that, and I accept myself; I love myself.

d) Even though *I do not think it safe for me* to have _____ dissolved, *I do think it is safe for me.* I am OK with that, I accept that, and I accept myself; I love myself.

e) Even though *I do not think it safe for others* to have _____ dissolved, *I do think it is safe for others.* I am OK with that, I accept that, and I accept myself; I love myself.

f) Even though *I do think I will lose my identity* to have _____dissolved, *I do not think* I will lose my identity. I am OK with that, I accept that, and I accept myself; I love myself.

5) The statement that you select will need to be spoken and repeated **three times** and, as with

the prior steps, you need to emphasize your words and use great expression and energy as you speak these words. You are not reading text from a magazine!

6) Then proceed to look within and quickly, without too much thought, rate where your prior difficult anxiety issue is on the scale of 0 to 10.

This procedure is used when the REIN process does not change your rating number after several attempts. This process for hidden objections is successful 80% of the time. If not, then take time to review all the steps in REIN, looking for a step that was not done in exact accordance with directions (or even omitted accidentally). If the rating is still higher than desired, it is time to find additional assistance from a local licensed therapist, specifically one that is trained and certified in Energy Psychology.

**Conclusion**

Anxiety as a state of emotional being is ruinous for us. Sadly, although we may want to rid ourselves of this degree of fear, anxiety (and the "story" with it) has become so woven in the fabric of our being that there is greater fear in finding resolution. The anxiety state of being prevents us from being resourceful and, importantly, from finding and residing our forgotten natural state of loving bliss. Anxiety, as a degree of fear, resides in our body as

PART THREE **THE PROBLEM SOLUTIONS**

a result of our disrupted energy fields. It devastates the body. Our disrupted energy fields are the cause of this stuck state, but they can be normalized and equilibrium can be achieved.

This book is the result of my desire to share a profound yet simple method that dissolves anxiety and that benefits you in moving toward your natural state. This book has been prompted by my success in conveying and teaching this process to people all over the world—from 10 year olds to 71 year olds—over the last four years. The REIN process is a rapid and effective tool for you to use. REIN has been designed to be a self-administered method. Like many new things, there may be some awkwardness and a bit of ineptness, but you will improve quickly with but a few trials. REIN is straightforward; you will realize the results and effectiveness immediately and it is something that you can test. Attention and effort have been directed to provide you beforehand with sufficient background knowledge so that you will feel comfortable and confident in using REIN.

Namaste.

# About the Author

Dr. Johnny Kenley DC is an Energy Therapist & Practitioner. He is a physician (specializing in physical medicine for 25 yrs.), an Applied Kinesiologist, and an acupuncturist (traditional & medical) for a similar number of years. His prior academic background comprises both undergraduate and graduate degrees in physics, mathematics, and business administration. He has since acquired a degree in human biology and a graduate degree in clinical human nutrition. His advanced certifications include post doctorate training with American College of Nutrition, with the Academy of Certified Nutritional Specialists, in Applied Kinesiology, in Visceral Manipulation, in Kinesio-taping, in Medical Acupuncture (Diplomat), in Manipulation Under Anesthesia, and in Energy Psychology and NLP. He has continually secured ongoing formal training and gained acumen in clinical hypnosis, counseling (with the Big Brother, VOA homeless shelters, women coming off welfare, prisoners with jail chaplaincy, restorative justice, academic consulting / coaching, creative problem solving with school children—Odyssey of the Mind, EST, theological study for Deaconry, cranial-sacral therapy, Emotional Freedom Therapy, Thought Field Therapy, and Neuro-Emotive Technique. He is a meditator and teaches Kundalini meditation.

Dr. Johnny has worked as a farmhand, auto mechanic, a

janitor, surveyor, physicist, a machine-language computer programmer, tactical nuclear weapons analyst, physician (in physical medicine), counselor, Traditional Chinese Medicine practitioner, a technical analyst and covert operative in intelligence services, coach, nutritionist, jail chaplain and lay minister, college instructor, entrepreneur, and Energy Psychologist and therapist.

A traumatic brain injury and subsequent 4 years of neurocognitive rehabilitation completely transformed and channeled his life in a wonderful direction of service; leading Dr. Johnny Kenley to spend the rest of his life giving himself away. He has spent the last 4 years developing his REIN process, treating clients from as young as 7 years old, as well as teaching workshops on four continents, where individuals learned REIN to be able to dissolve their anxieties by themselves. He is currently bringing these workshops and training to the United States for individuals, groups, organizations, colleges, and businesses. His U.S. charitable nonprofit corporation **(Global Medical Aid and Education)** is the recipient of all book royalties and all revenue from workshops and speaking engagements.

# Disclaimer

The information provided in this book is designed to provide helpful information on the subjects discussed. This book is sold with the understanding that the author is not engaged to render any type of psychological, medical, legal, or any other kind of professional advice within this book. This book is not a consultation or direction for medical or psychological care, nor a substitute for such. This book is not intended to be used for, nor should it be used, to **diagnose** or treat any clinical medical or mental condition. For diagnosis or treatment of any medical problem consult your own licensed physician, psychiatrist, psychologist, or licensed health care practitioner. The author is not engaging in any doctor patient relationship and reading of this material does not imply that. The reader should not rely on the information in this book as a substitute for medical advice from your physician or other licensed professional health care provider. The author is not responsible for any specific health needs, before, during, or after reading this book that may require medical supervision and is not liable for any damages or negative consequences from any action or application of the information contained within the book. References are provided for informational purposes only and do not constitute endorsement of any treatment approaches, books, or other actions.

# Afterward

You will be able to acquire , at no charge, a single page "cheat-sheet" that shows the seven steps of the REIN process. This can be accomplished by visiting my website...

anxietysolutionsnow.com

This will enable you to have a handy and easy way to facilitate your practice, without having to page through the book. You will also be able to obtain an illustrative copy of the appropriate acupuncture points and the Chakras, again at no charge.

I am hopeful that you have found this book easy to read, understandable, entertaining and informative. Most of all, I hope that you now have an excited interest in resolving your particular anxiety issues by yourself.

Upon your finishing this book, I would kindly ask for a modicum of your time for an Amazon review.

45264306R00116

Made in the USA
Lexington, KY
22 September 2015